SCHUMANN

THE INTERNATIONAL LIBRARY OF MUSIC

FOR HOME AND STUDIO

STUDY MATERIAL

IN TWO BOOKS

A Manual of Practical Instruction in Pianoforte Playing Combining all the Essentials from the beginning of Grade One through Grade Four

Compiled and Edited from the World's Greatest Composers and Authorities

WITH ORIGINAL PIECES, TECHNICAL EXERCISES AND EXPLANATORY TEXT

BY

CHARLES DENNÉE

PROFESSOR OF PIANOFORTE PLAYING IN THE NEW ENGLAND CONSERVATORY OF MUSIC BOSTON, MASSACHUSETTS

VOLUME II

GRADES THREE AND FOUR

1958

THE UNIVERSITY SOCIETY, INC.
Educational Publishers
NEW YORK

In addition to a wealth of new material, this new edition of The International Library of Music combines the best features of its highly successful predecessors; namely:

Famous Songs and Those Who Made Them .... Copyright 1896
The World's Best Music .... Copyright 1897
Paderewski—Century Library of Music .... Copyright 1900
Modern Music and Musicians .... Copyright 1912
La Mejor Musica del Mundo .... Copyright 1917
The University Course of Music Study .... Copyright 1920
The International Library of Music .... Copyright 1925
A Melhor Musica do Mundo .... Copyright 1930
The International Library of Music .... Copyright 1934

MANUFACTURED IN THE U. S. A.

TABLE OF CONTENTS

VOLUME II

GRADE III

		PAGE
For the developing of finger independence; double notes and Progressive Five-finger Exercises	SCHMITT, from Op. 16	1
For perfecting the passing under of the thumb and crossing over of the fingers		5
Chords and Arpeggios		8
Major Scales in Double Thirds		10
Minor Scales in Double Thirds		11

STUDIES

Study, *G major*, Op. 120, No. 5	DUVERNOY	12
Study, *G major*, Op. 20, No. 4	LE COUPPEY	13
Study, *C minor*, Op. 29, No. 7	BERTINI	14
Prelude, *F major*	J. S. BACH	15
Prelude, *C minor*	J. S. BACH	16
Study, *C major*	MORTIMER WILSON	18
Study, *G major*	LEMOINE	20
Study, *B-flat*	CZERNY	22
Study, *C major*	LEMOINE	24
Etude, *C major*, Op. 299, No. 3	CZERNY	26
Etude, *C major*, Op. 299, No. 4	CZERNY	28
Etude, *C major*, Op. 299, No. 6	CZERNY	30
Etude, *C major*, Op. 299, No. 11	CZERNY	32
Etude, *G major*, Op. 299, No. 18	CZERNY	34
Study, *A minor*, Op. 29, No. 18	BERTINI	36
Study, *B-flat*, Op. 20, No. 13	LE COUPPEY	37
Study, *C minor*, Op. 29, No. 6	BERTINI	38
Study, *G minor*, Op. 29, No. 3	BERTINI	39
Study, *C major*, Op. 61, No. 1	BERENS	40
Study, *C major*, Op. 299, No. 2	CZERNY	41
Study, *A minor*, Op. 45, No. 2	HELLER	42
Study, *B major*, Op. 821, No. 33	CZERNY	43
Study, *E major*, Op. 821, No. 35	CZERNY	43
Study, *B major*, Op. 821, No. 43	CZERNY	44
Study, *C major*, Op. 61, No. 5	BERENS	44
Study, *C major*, Op. 61, No. 9	BERENS	46
Study, *G major*, Op. 61, No. 11	BERENS	48
Study, *C major*, Op. 29, No. 22 (Arr.)	BERTINI	49
Study, *B-flat*, Op. 45, No. 16	HELLER	50
Study, *C major*, Op. 16, No. 8	A. SCHMITT	52
Study, *C major*, Op. 120, No. 8	DUVERNOY	53
Study, *G major*	LEMOINE	54

		PAGE
Study, *G major*, Op. 37, No. 49	LEMOINE	56
Study, *E-flat*, Op. 636, No. 12	CZERNY	57
Study, *C major*, Op. 299, No. 7	CZERNY	58
Study, *D minor*, Op. 45, No. 15	HELLER	60
Study, *C major*, Op. 821, No. 107	CZERNY	61
Study, *C major*, Op. 821, No. 108	CZERNY	61
Study, *E minor*, Op. 50, No. 11	HASERT	62
Study, *F major*, Op. 299, No. 12	CZERNY	64
Study, *B-flat minor*, Op. 821, No. 76	CZERNY	65
Study, *C minor*, Op. 38, No. 23	LOESCHHORN	66
Study, *E-flat*, Op. 299, No. 25	CZERNY	68
Study, *C major*, Op. 299, No. 32	CZERNY	70
Two-Voice Invention, *C major*, No. I	J. S. BACH	72
Two-Voice Invention, *F major*, No. VIII	J. S. BACH	73
Etude, *E-flat*, Op. 16, No. 24	SCHMITT	74
Study, *C major*	BERTINI	76
Etude, *C major*	SCHMITT	78
Study, *D major*	CZERNY	79
Study, *G major*	CZERNY	80
Study, *C major*	BERTINI	82
Etude	BELA BARTOK	83
Study, *G major*	SCHMITT	84
Octave Studies	CZERNY	85

GRADE IV

TECHNICAL EXERCISES

Introductory remarks	89
Exercises, by Tausig and Pischna	90

STUDIES

Study, No. I, *C major*	CRAMER	100
Study, No. XIII, *A major*	CRAMER	102
Study, No. XXII, *F-Sharp minor*	CRAMER	104
Study, Op. 740, No. 49	CZERNY	106
Study, *A-flat*	CZERNY	107
Study, No. LI, *F minor*	CRAMER	108
Study, *E major*	SCHMITT	110
Study, *A minor*	SCHMITT	112
Study, *B-flat*	SCHMITT	118
Study, *E-flat*	SCHMITT	120
Study, No. IX, *G major*	CRAMER	124
Study, *C major*, No. XXXI	CLEMENTI	126
Study, *F major*, No. LXVIII	CRAMER	131
Study, No. XII, *A minor*	CRAMER	134
Invention, Two-Voice, No. IV, *D minor*	J. S. BACH	136
Invention, Two-Voice, No. XIV, *B-flat*	J. S. BACH	138
Invention, Two-Voice, No. XV, *B-minor*	J. S. BACH	140
Invention, Two-Voice, No. IX, *F minor*	J. S. BACH	142
Study, No. XVIII, *D minor*	CRAMER	144
Study, No. LVI, *D major*	CRAMER	146
Study, *F-sharp minor*	SCHMITT	148

		PAGE
Study, No. LXV, *E minor*	Cramer	152
Study, No. LIV, *C major*	Cramer	154
Study, No. LXIX, *D minor*	Cramer	156
Exercise, *D major*	Czerny	158
Exercise, *G major*	Czerny	159
Study, No. XXXVII, *B-flat major*	Cramer	160
Study, No. XXXII, *D minor*	Cramer	162
Study, *D minor*, Op. 740, No. 37	Czerny	165
Study, *F major*, Op. 740	Czerny	168
Study, *C major*, Op. 16, No. 4	Schmitt	171
Study, No. XCV, *C major*	Clementi	172
Study, *E-flat major*, Op. 740, No. 5	Czerny	176
Study, *A minor*, Op. 740, No. 41	Czerny	180
Study, *D major*, Op. 740, No. 21	Czerny	182
Study, No. XVI, *C major*	Clementi	184
Study, *A minor*, Op. 740, No. 31	Czerny	188
Study, No. XVII, *C major*	Clementi	191
Invention, Three-Voice, No. IV, *D minor*	J. S. Bach	194
Invention, Three-Voice, No. VI, *E major*	J. S. Bach	196
Study, No. LXXVIII, *G major*	Clementi	198
Study, No. XLIV, *F minor*	Clementi	201

THIRD GRADE

Special Exercises For Developing Finger Technic

DOUBLE NOTES

Continuation of Schmitt Preparatory Studies, Op. 16, from Grade II.

Transpose to easier major Keys; eventually to all major and minor Keys.

Repeated Double Notes With Three Fingers Anchored

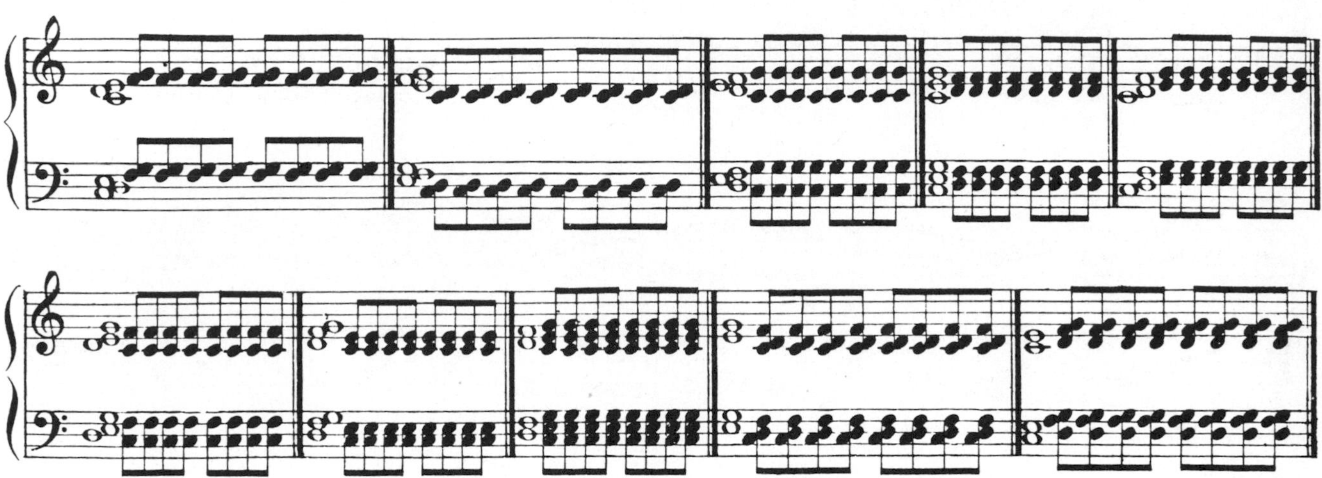

Avoid stiffness or strain in all exercises holding Keys; independence is the point to be gained.

Progressive Five-Finger Exercises

The following Exercises should be practiced, ascending and descending, over the éntire length of the keyboard, in every Key, both Major and Minor.

1 2
5 4
1 2
5 4
5 4
1 2
2 1
3 2
4 5
3 4
4 5
3 4
2 1
3 2
1
1 2
5
5 4
5
5 4 3 2
1
1 2 3 4
2 3 1 3
2 3 4 2 4
4 3 5 3
4 3 2 4 2
3
3
4 3 5 3
4 3 5 4
3 2 4 2
2 3 1 3
2 3 1 2
3 4 2 4

Special Exercises

For perfecting the passing under of the thumb and crossing over of the fingers

SCALES

ARPEGGIOS

The following exercises are designed for separate hand practise.

Right Hand

Common Chord

Left Hand

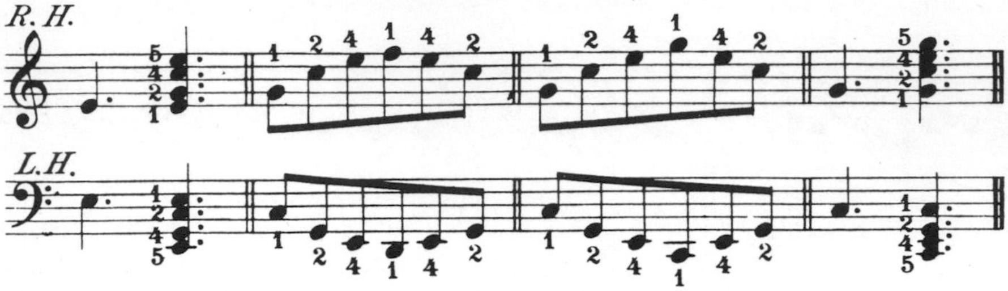

R.H.

L.H.

Transpose into every key. In chords which begin on a black key, use the chromatic intervals passing the thumb under as follows:

R.H.

L.H.

R.H.

L.H.

R.H.

L.H.

R.H.

Dominant Sevenths

L.H.

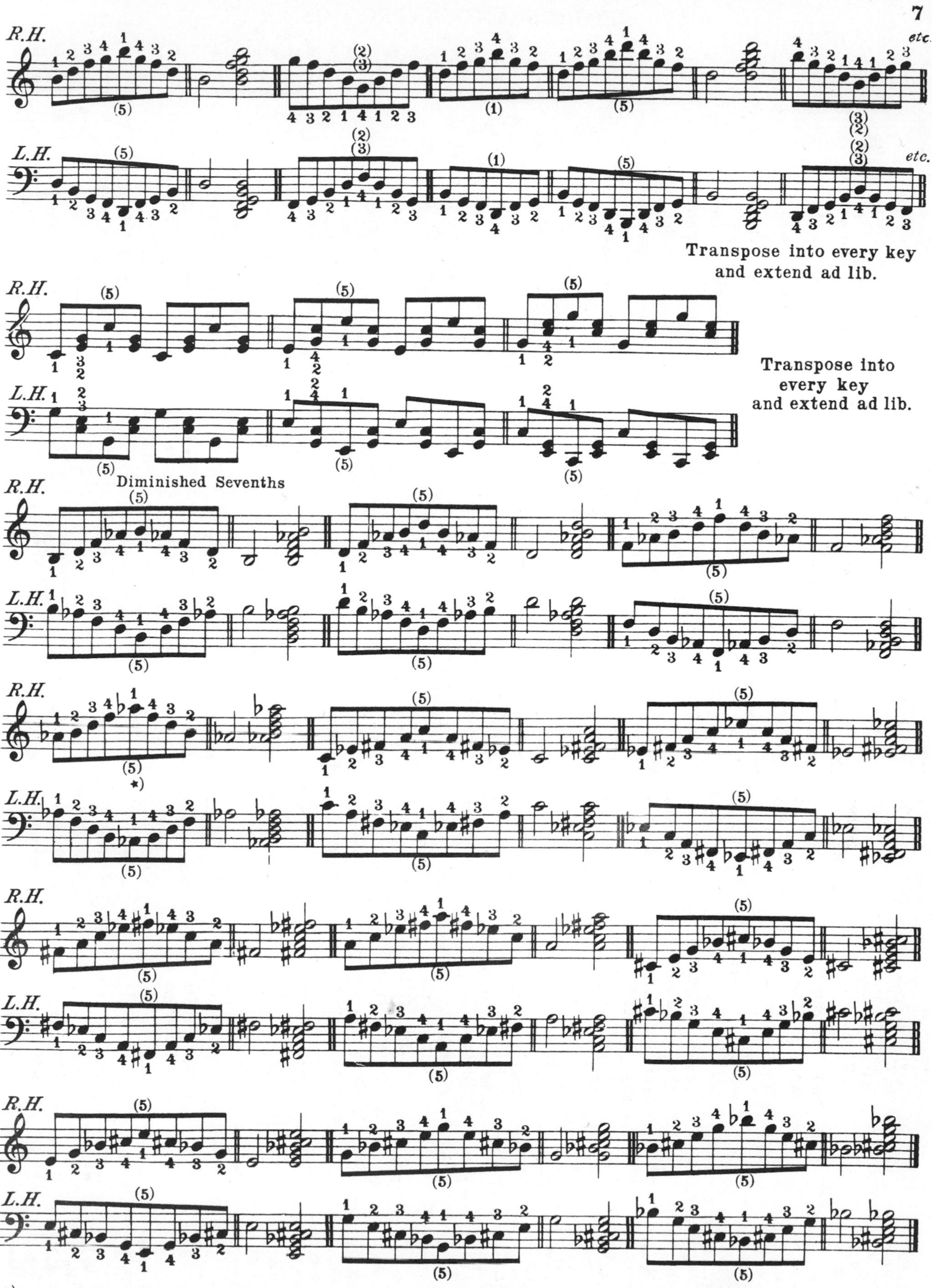

*) As a matter of practise the use of the thumb on the black keys is strongly recommended

After a review of the chords and arpeggios of C, G, D, A, E, B and F Major, and A, E, D, G, C and F Minor, as given in the Second Grade, practise the following chords, applying to each Key the three model arpeggio forms. Play all arpeggios over a compass of four octaves; hands at first separate, then together.

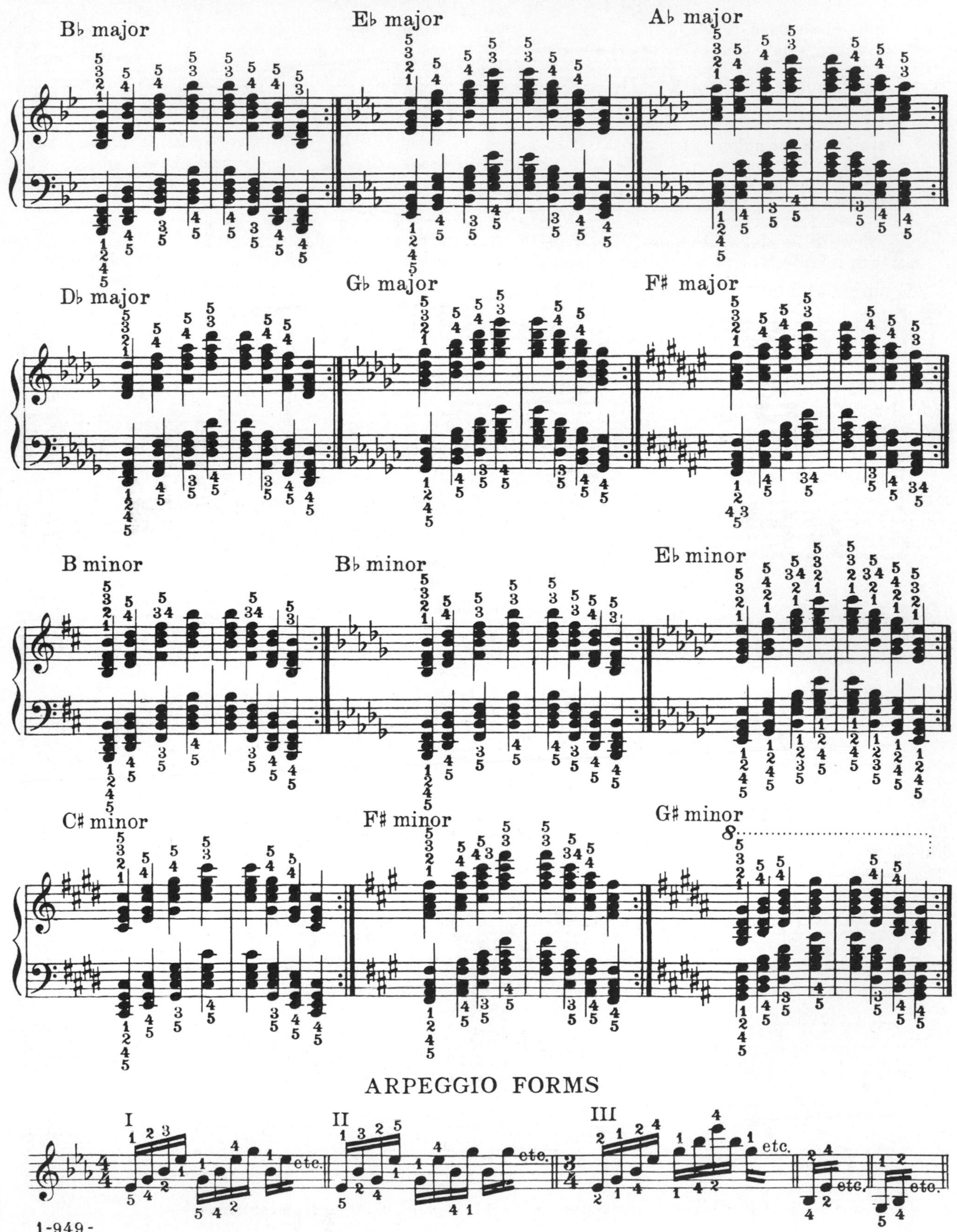

SCALES

Continue practising the easier major and minor scales for greater speed, adding new ones until all the scales are learned. Then play them in groups of two, three, and six, and in dotted rhythms; also with two notes against one and other variations from the plain scale.

OCTAVES

Pupils whose hands are large enough to permit them to stretch an octave without straining the back of the hand or the wrist should now begin to practise the scales in octaves at a moderate speed. Play for very short periods at first – never long enough to tire the wrist. Easy wrist action and moderate force will give the best results. Do not play loudly until perfect control and facility are gained.

DOUBLE THIRDS

Only the easier major and minor scales should be practised in the Third Grade, reserving the more difficult ones for the Fourth Grade. Play all the scales in broken Thirds. This is often done first, to establish the fingering for the Double Thirds.

DOMINANT SEVENTH CHORDS

Review the Dominant Seventh Chords applying the three arpeggio models in C, G, D, A and F and B♭ Major and their relative Minors, as given in the Second Grade. Also apply the arpeggio models to the following chords:

ARPEGGIO MODELS FOR SEVENTHS

DIMINISHED SEVENTH CHORDS

Review the diminished Seventh chords and arpeggios of C, F, D, A, and G Minor, as given in the Second Grade, applying the arpeggio models given for the dominant Seventh. Also apply the models to the following chords, practising all arpeggios over a compass of two, three and four octaves.

Major Scales in Double Thirds

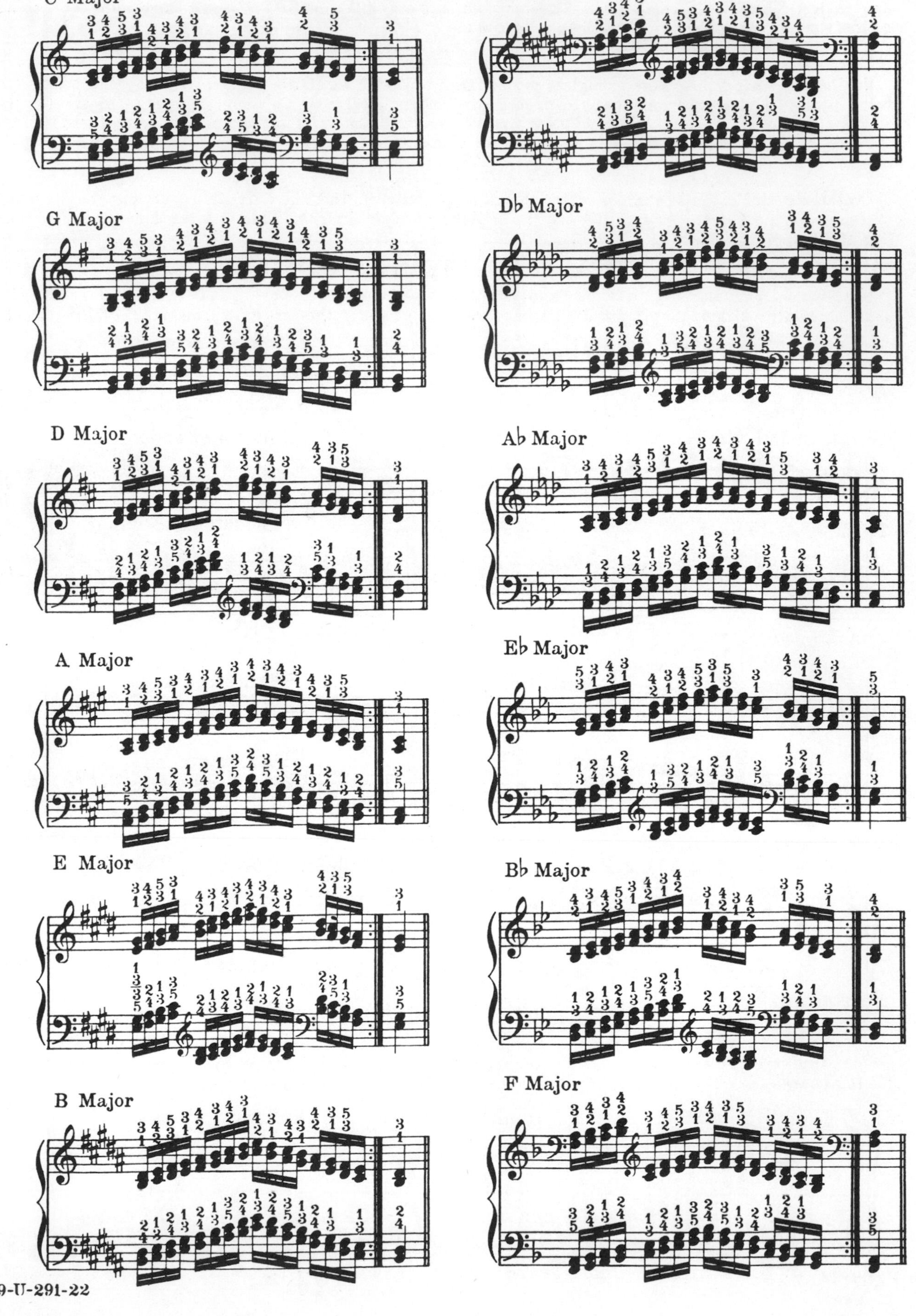

Minor Scales in Double Thirds

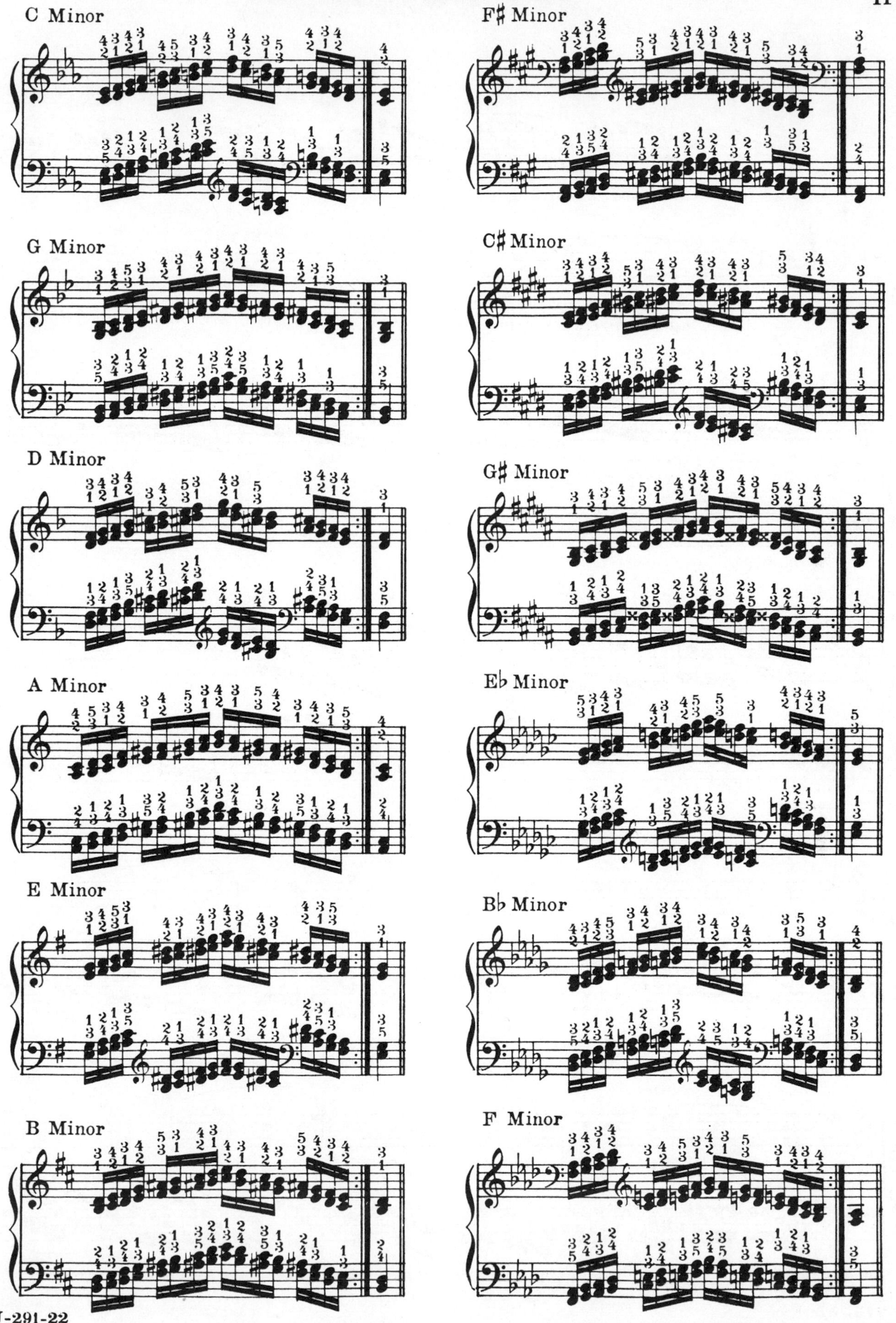

Edited by
CHARLES DENNÉE

Allegro moderato

Adapted from DUVERNOY, Op. 120, № 5

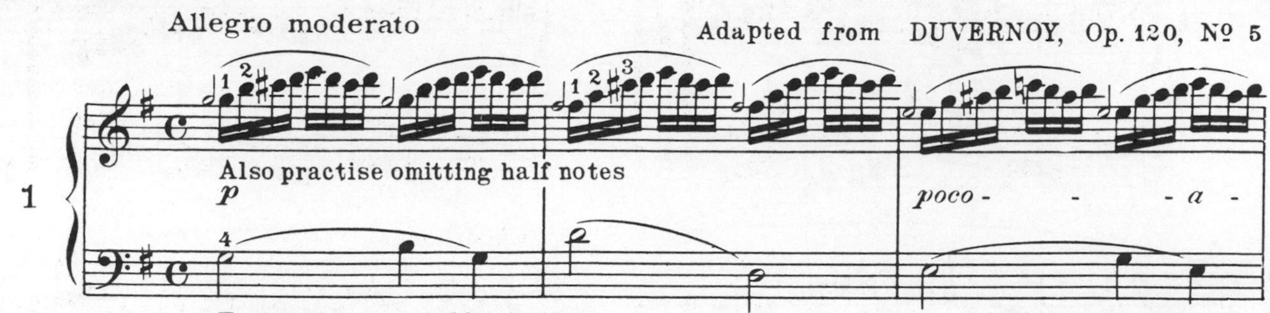

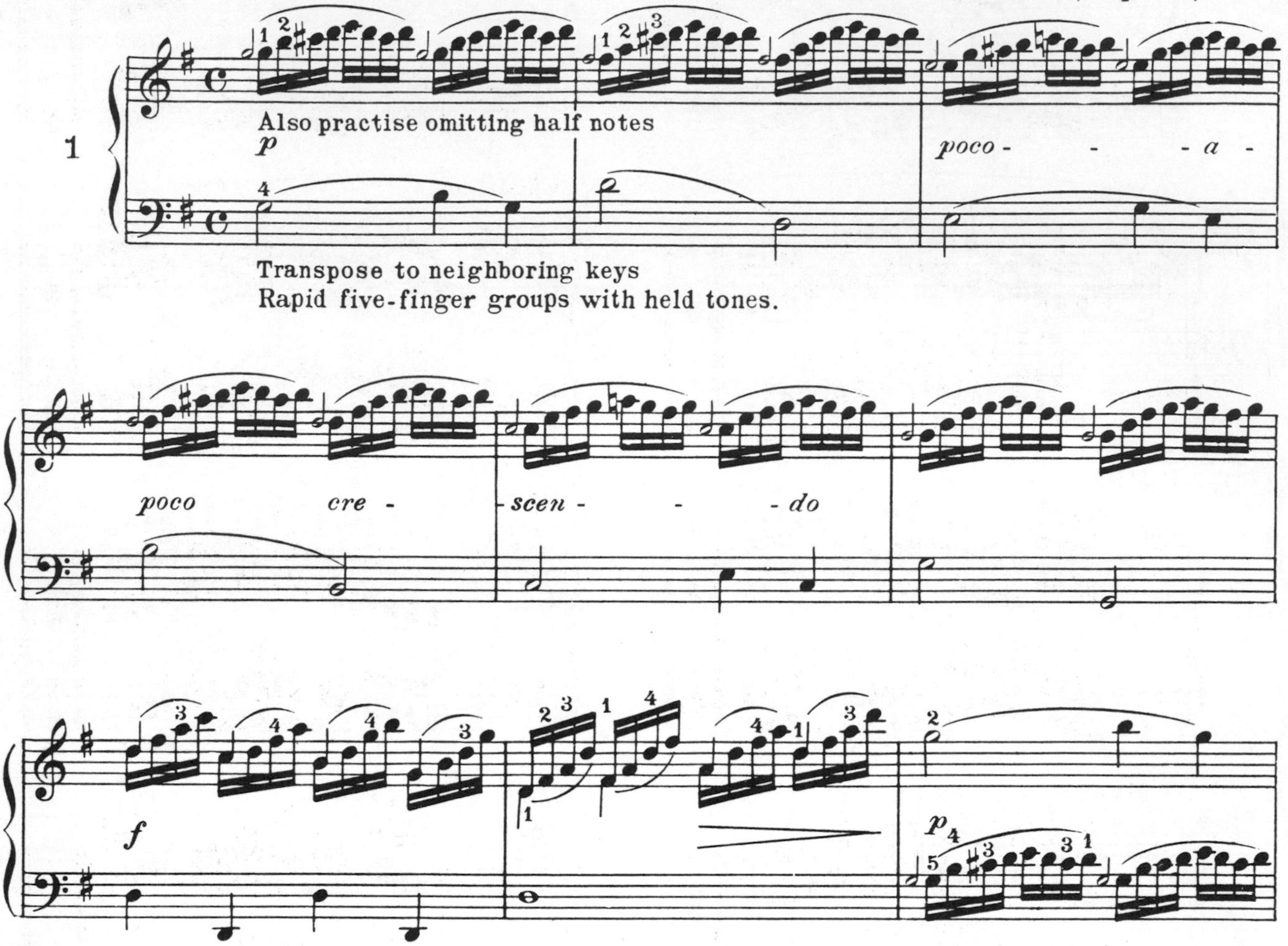
1
Also practise omitting half notes
p
poco - - a -
Transpose to neighboring keys
Rapid five-finger groups with held tones.
poco cre - scen - - do
f
p
cre - - scen - - do
f

·Holding the half notes affords excellent practice for security and independence in the first slow practice

Edited by
CHARLES DENNÉE

Rapid groups for Finger Crossing, with accented melodic tones.

Allegro moderato (♩=126) LE COUPPEY, Op. 20, Nº 4

Practise slowly and with finger precision at first, then work for lightness and agility in the finger action

STUDY

For fluency and precision in brilliant finger passages.

BERTINI
Op. 29, Nº 7

PRELUDE

PRELUDE

f
decresc.
p
cresc.
f
dim.
allarg.
f

STUDY

MORTIMER WILSON

Moderato

mf
mp
cresc.
f
dim.
p cresc. sempre
f

LEGATO STUDY

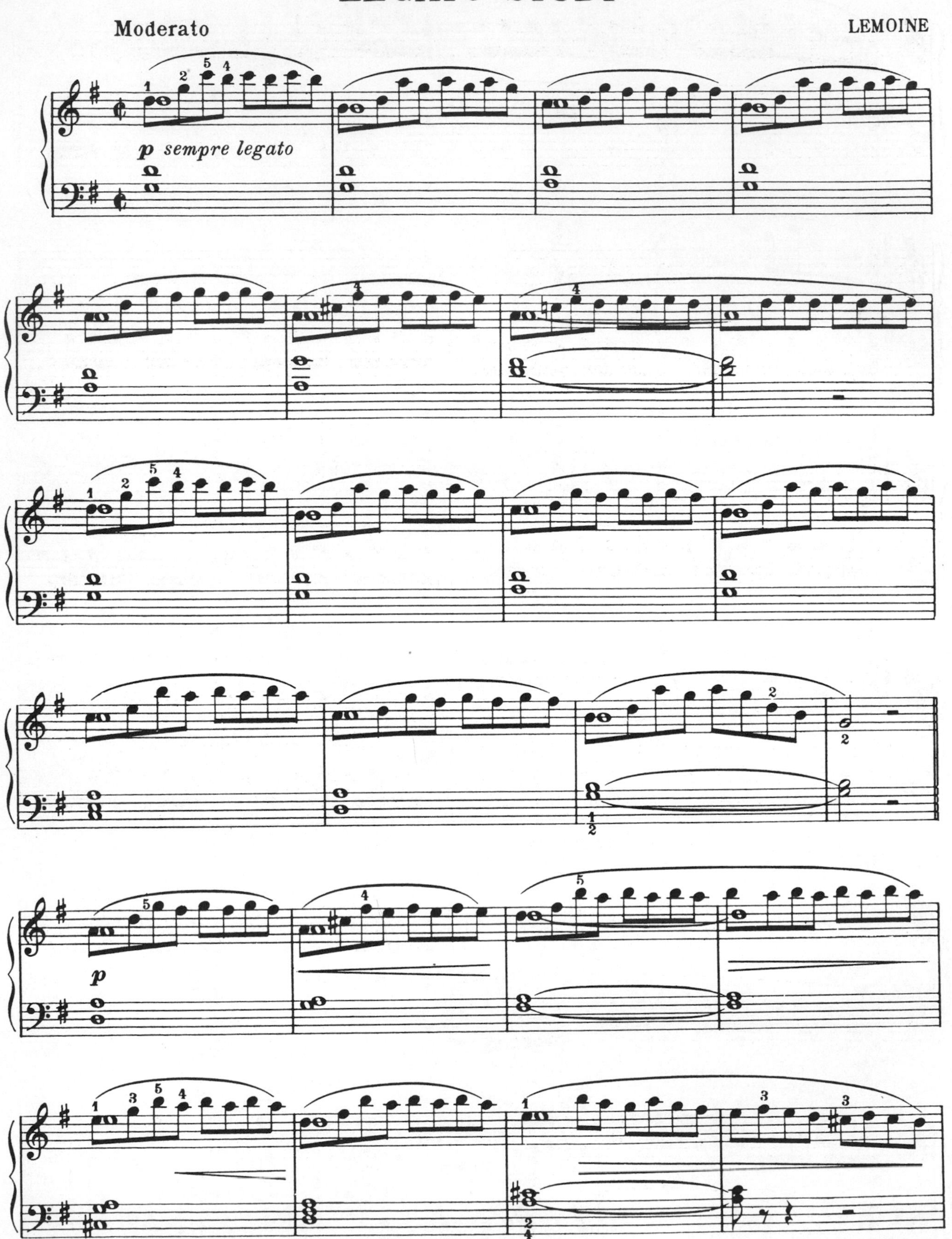

STUDY

CARL CZERNY

Presto

pp cantando

pp

mf

dim.
p
dim.
pp
calando

STUDY

LEMOINE

p
f
ff

ETUDE
C MAJOR

C. CZERNY
Op. 299, Nº 3

f
ff
8

ETUDE

C MAJOR

C. CZERNY
Op. 299, № 4

p
cresc.
f
ff

ETUDE

C MAJOR

C. CZERNY
Op. 299, № 6

Molto Allegro

f
dim.
p
cresc.
cresc.
f
più f
Original
ff

ETUDE

C MAJOR

C. CZERNY
Op. 299, № 11

leggiero staccato
cresc.
cresc.
dim.
cresc.

STUDY
G MAJOR

CZERNY

Molto allegro

p

cresc.

segue

sf

cresc.

f

p
cresc.
f
più f
8
ff

Edited by
CHARLES DENNÉE

STUDY for firm staccato octaves and graceful short runs.

BERTINI, Op. 29, Nº 18

Allegretto (♩ = 112)

Edited by
CHARLES DENNÉE

For fluency and grace in rapid scale figures.

Allegro (♩ = 132)

LE COUPPEY Op. 20, № 13

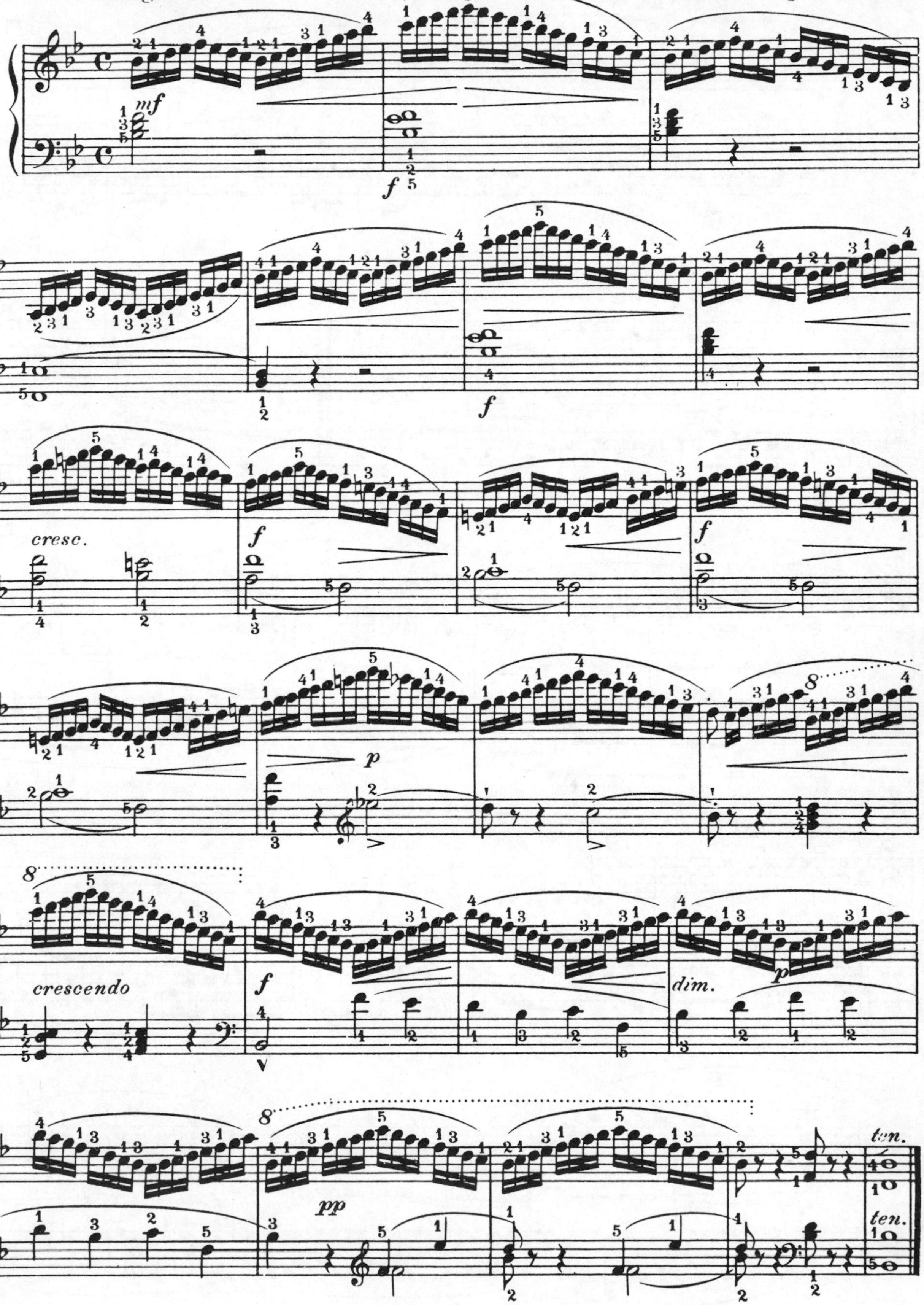

mf *f* *cresc.* *p* *crescendo* *dim.* *pp* *ten.*

STUDY for legato part playing against a contrapuntal figure.

STUDY

C MINOR

BERTINI Op 29 Nº 6

Allegro (♩ = 138)

Equality of Fingers in Varied Figures.

STUDY

Allegro (♩= 138)

BERTINI Op 29 № 3

STUDY. Scale positions in Sequence.

BERENS. Op. 61, №1

STUDY. Equality in Velocity Scale Passages.

STUDY

C MAJOR

CZERNY. Op. 299, No 2

STUDY. Rapid alternation of hands in short legato figure.

Edited by
CHARLES DENNÉE

HELLER, Op. 45, № 2.

 These two studies may be combined, ending with a repetition of the first.

Edited by
CHARLES DENNÉE

STUDY. Velocity in long Scales with strong accents.

CZERNY, Op. 821, Nº 43

Allegro

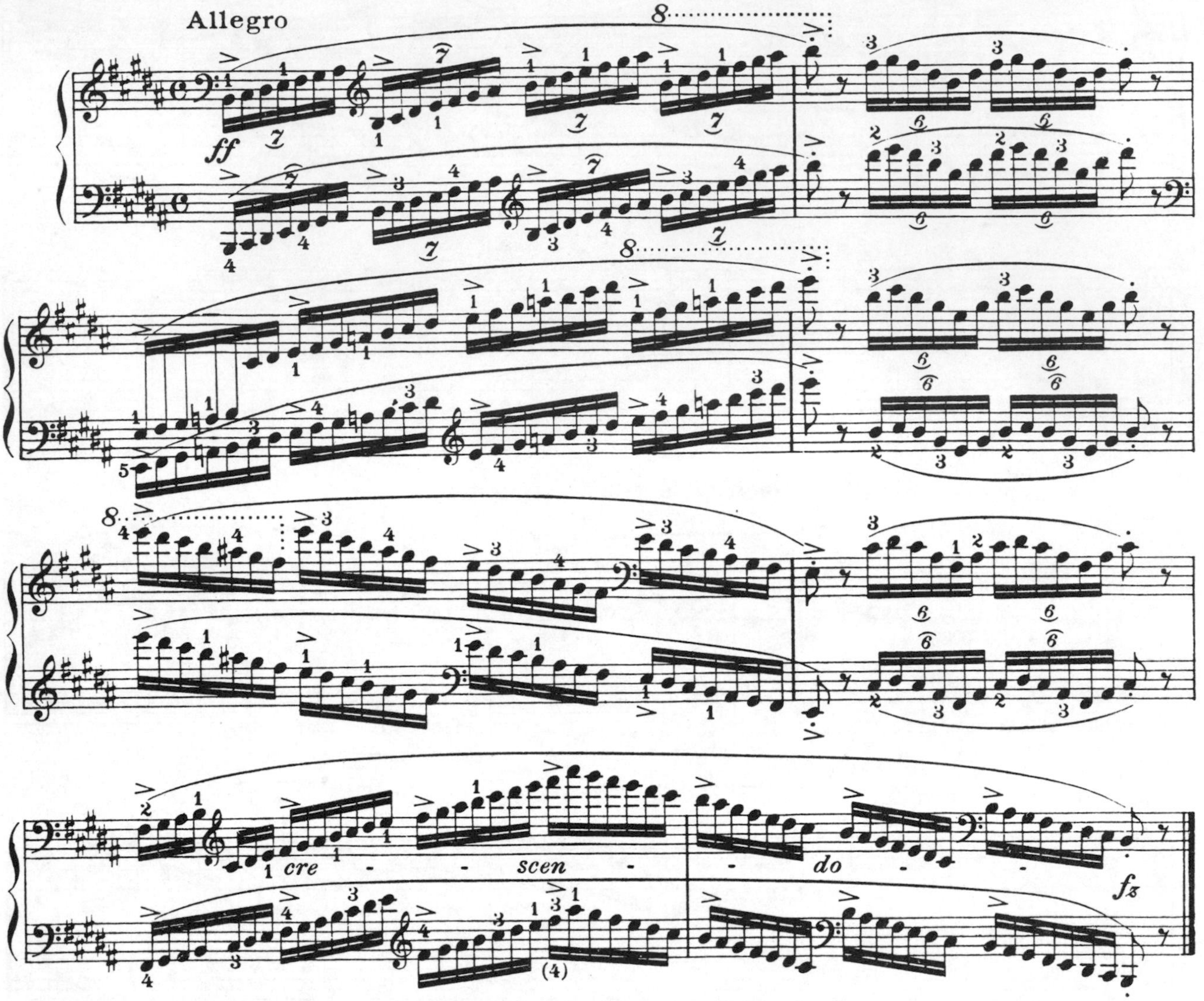

8
ff
cre - scen - do
fz

Review constantly for added speed and facility; transpose to neighboring keys.

Edited by
CHARLES DENNÉE

STUDY. Scale passages with melodic tones.

BERENS, Op. 61, Nº 5

Allegro risoluto

*) p

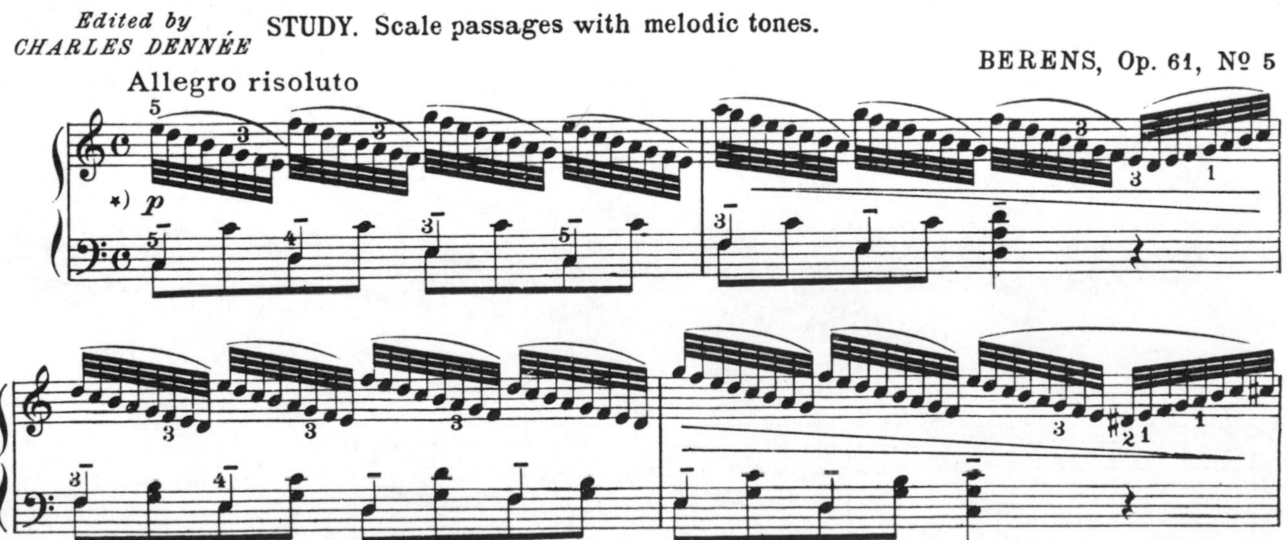

*) The first note of each scale group later becomes R. H. melody, while the bass melodic progression becomes first note of L. H. scale groups.

f
p
f
dim.

STUDY. Sweeping scales, with wrist action and positive rhythm.

BERENS, Op.61, No. 9

Allegro (♩ = 54)

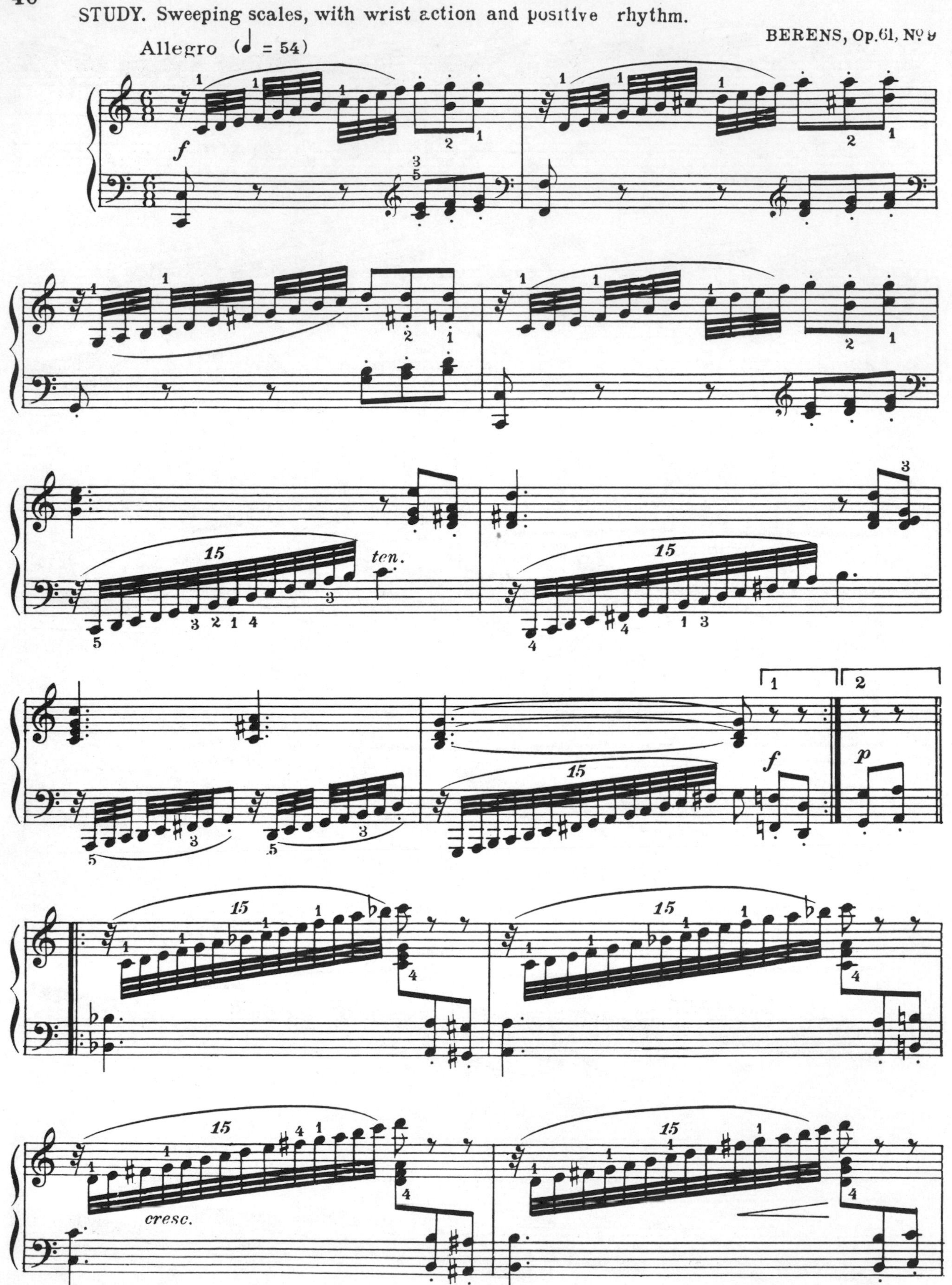

Dexterity in scale passages with legato chord accompaniment.

Edited by
CHARLES DENNÉE

BERENS. Op. 61, Nº 11

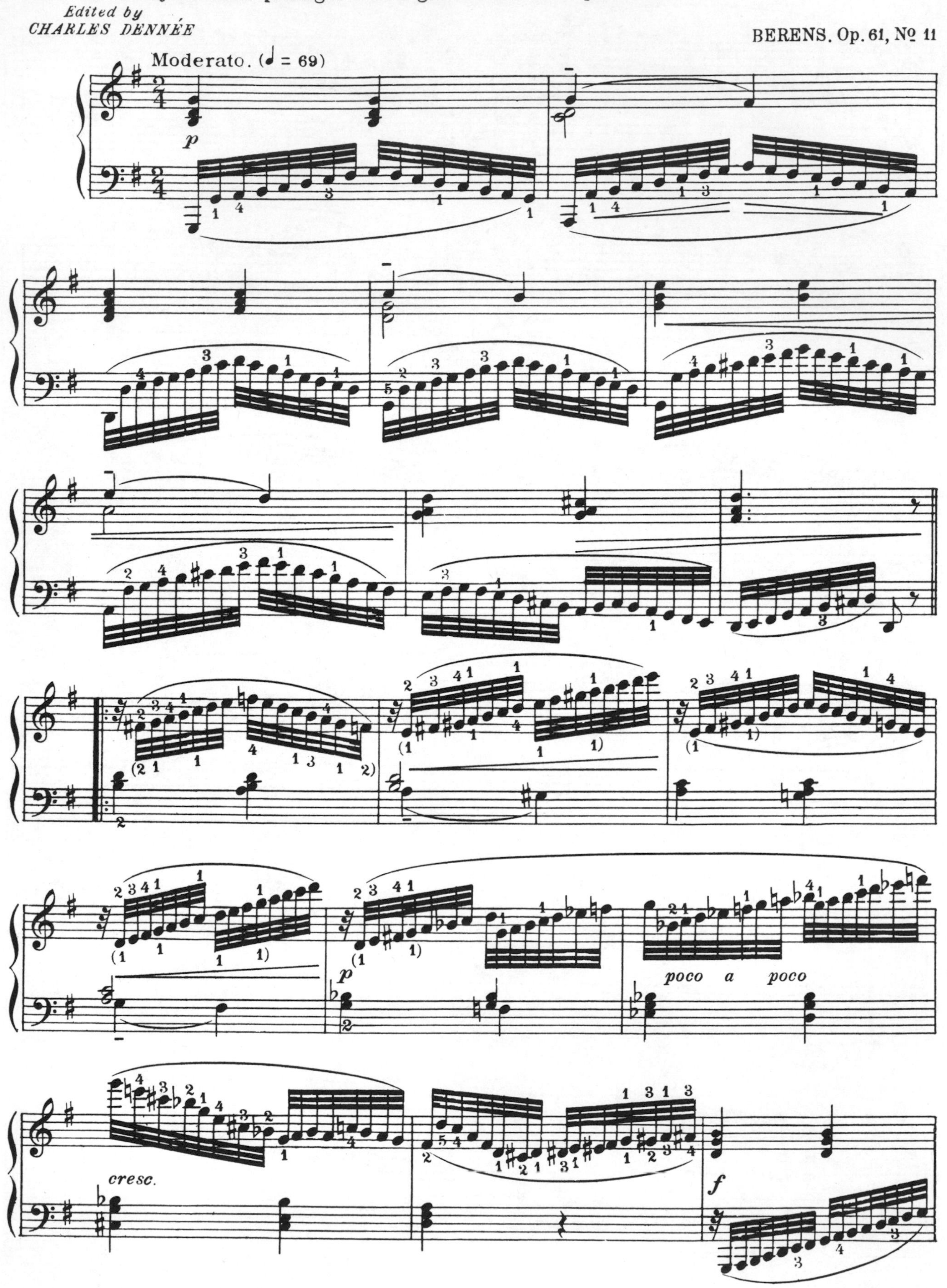

Edited by
CHARLES DENNÉE
OCTAVE STUDY, for fluency in wrist action.
Arreglo de
Arr. from BERTINI. Op. 29
Nº 22.
Allegretto. (♩= 116.)
cres - cen - do
Fine.
D. S.

STUDY. A singing melody with graceful broken chord accompaniment.

ST. HELLER
Op. 45, No. 16

mf
mf
f
riten.
p a tempo
dolce
mf
1.
2.
p delicamente
pp
pp

STUDY. Rapid scales and smoothness in wide legato stretches.

A. SCHMITT
Op. 16, No. 8

Flexibility and ease in continuous grand arpeggios.

DUVERNOY, Op. 120, No. 8

Allegro moderato (♩ = 126)

ETUDE

For facility in legato thirds.

LEMOINE

p
cresc.
f
p
cresc.
rit.
p a tempo
cresc.
p
poco rit.

Edited by
CHARLES DENNÉE

STUDY. Brilliancy in rapid staccato triads.

LEMOINE. Op. 37, No. 49

This study should be transposed to other keys as added proficiency is attained.

Equality in triad and seventh chord arpeggios.

Edited by
CHARLES DENNÉE

CZERNY, Op. 636, Nº 12

Do not attempt speed until the fingers feel sure at a slow tempo, then gradually increase to Allegro; eventually Presto.

STUDY for velocity in the left hand.

CZERNY, Op. 299, № 7

Molto Allegro (𝅗𝅥 = 104)

cresc.
f
dimin.
p
8
cresc.
f
dimin.
pp

Edited by
CHARLES DENNÉE

HELLER, Op. 45, № 15

STUDY. Massive Chords in Strict Rhythm

Practise very slowly and firmly, for precision, at first. Review constantly for speed and freedom.

Edited by
CHARLES DENNÉE

STUDY
E MINOR

HASERT, Op. 50, Nº 11

Allegretto con moto

For thumb passing and finger crossing.

ff
p
dim.
pp
piu dim.
pp
dim.
pp
dim.
ppp

STUDY to develop power with velocity in grand arpeggios.

Molto allegro (𝅗𝅥 = 92) CZERNY, Op. 299, Nº 12

STUDY
B-FLAT MINOR
Allegro
CZERNY, Op. 821, № 76

STUDY for security in rapid short arpeggio groups

LOESCHHORN, Op. 38, № 23

sf
m.d.
m.g.
p
ff
Ped.
ap-
ten.
passionato
ten.
sf
p tranquillo
crescendo
ff energico
ff

STUDY for endurance in perpetual motion passages.

CZERNY, Op. 299, № 25

Edited by
CHARLES DENNEE

Equality in sweeping arpeggios with alternating hands.

CZERNY, Op. 299, Nº 32.

Practise for accuracy and distinctness and finger equality at first, gradually increasing speed when these qualities are mastered.

40 – 775 – 42

sf *f* *p* *cre - - scen - - do - - - -*

f *sf* *ff*

fp leggiero *poco - a - poco - cre - - scen - do -*

f *ff* *sf*

TWO-VOICE INVENTION, No I

BACH

TWO-VOICE INVENTION

F MAJOR, Nº VIII

J. S. BACH

ETUDE

A. SCHMITT

cresc.

p legato

f marcato e legato

dim.

p

mp

cresc.

f

ff

sf

STUDY

Allegro

BERTINI

f
8
ff

ETUDE

C MAJOR

ALOYS SCHMITT

Allegro

STUDY

CZERNY

STUDY

TONE REPETITION

CZERNY

p
simile
simile
cresc.
f
sf

STUDY

BERTINI

Andante

simile

p

cresc.

il basso legato

p

cresc.

La melodia legata

mf

Fine

simile

rall.

p

D. C. al Fine

ETUDE

For the Hungarian cantilena
and Rhythmic Style

BÉLA BÁRTOK

STUDY

OCTAVE STUDY

CZERNY

cresc.
poco rit.
OCTAVE STUDY
Allegro comodo
CZERNY

f
p dolce
cresc.
dim.

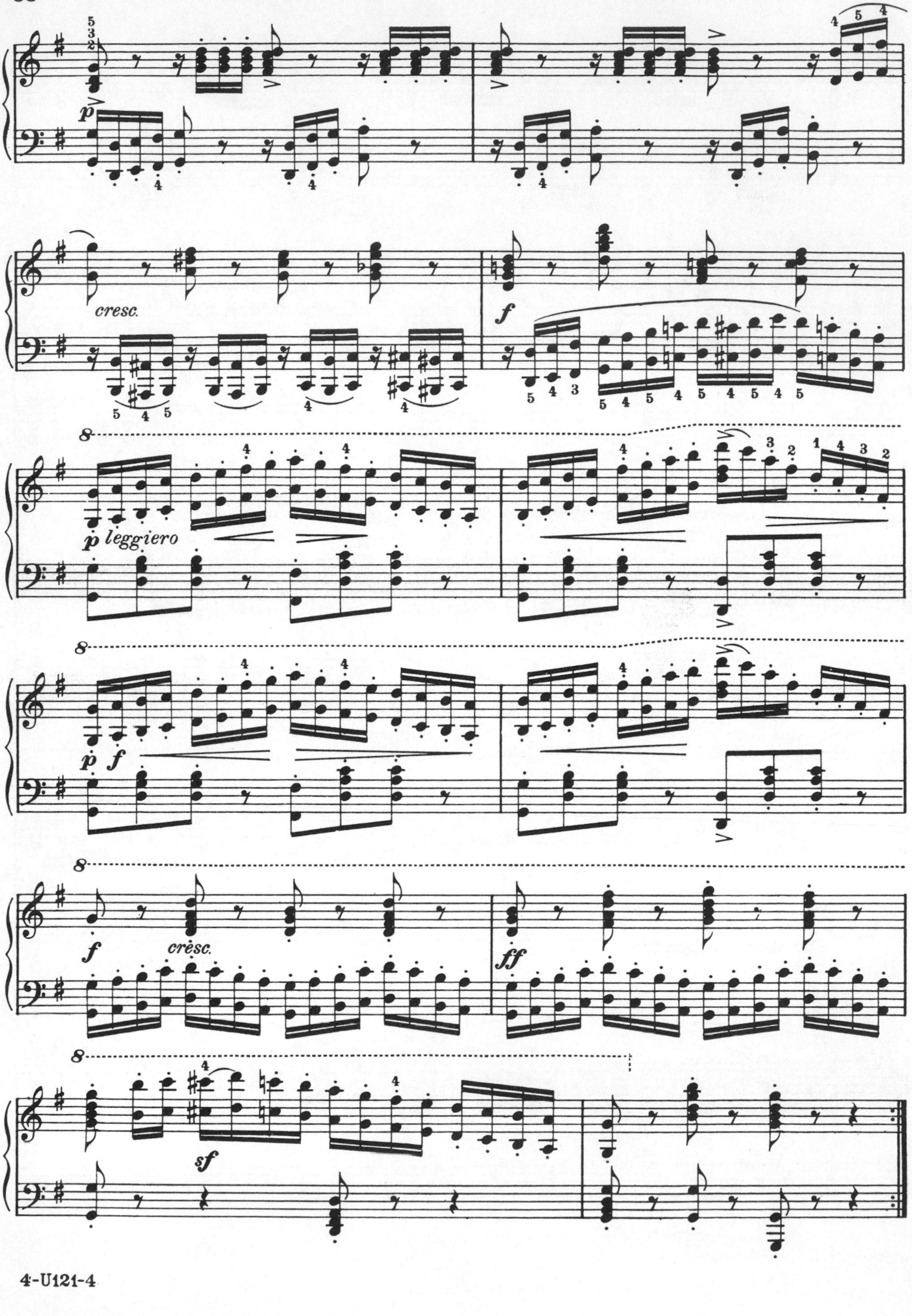
p
cresc.
f
8
p leggiero
8
p f
8
f
cresc.
ff
8
sf

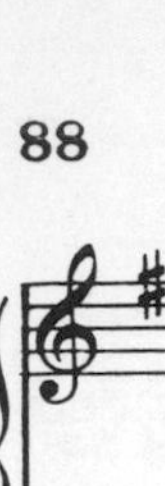

FOURTH GRADE

SPECIAL DAILY TECHNICAL EXERCISES

These exercises are designed for developing skill, strength, and independent control of the hands and fingers and to prepare the pupil for the difficulties and new technical problems that will be encountered in the more advanced stages of pianoforte playing.

These select exercises should be played slowly and accurately with separate hands at first. The fingers must function with equality of muscular control, and with perfection of motion, position and action.

To attain the full benefit of the fundamental five-finger exercises, the variants must be played in every major and minor Key. Keep the fingers properly curved when playing on the black keys, the lifting and playing motions as perfect as when in the Key of C Major.

With many of the exercises there is a model to be transposed chromatically through all the Keys. In each instance the first notes of the next Key are given at the end of the model. The non-transposing exercises are to be played also in every Key, using straight transpositions, in place of the modulatory progression.

Select from these special technical exercises those that fit the needs and the hands of the individual pupil. Many are given in order that this selection may cover a wide range. Omit until later any which develop the least tendency towards straining of the wrist, hand or fingers.

SCALES

All the scales are to be played with increasing fluency and speed, over a compass of at least four octaves; more where it is possible to do so. A speed of 120 to a quarter note, played in sixteenth notes, should be reached by the end of the grade.

Rhythmic variants should be applied to the scales: two against one, three against one, two against three, and dotted groupings, with accents in groups of two, three, four, and six; in staccato and legato combined, and other obvious combinations.

CHORDS

The triads and full chords and Dominant and Diminished Sevenths should be played in the regular order of Root, first inversion, second inversion, third inversion, over a compass of one octave; then over two or more octaves. Also play them in skips from each chord to the same chord an octave higher.

BROKEN CHORDS AND ARPEGGIOS

In so far as possible apply all the directions given for playing the scales. Develop flexibility of thumb, and ease in passing the hands over the keyboard while the fingers are playing.

DOUBLE THIRDS

Play in all Keys, gradually increasing the speed to a metronome speed of 92 to a quarter note, played in sixteenth notes.

OCTAVES

Play the scales and the grand arpeggios in octaves in all Keys at a comfortable tempo. In all octave playing, allow speed to develop gradually. Avoid wrist stiffness, fatigue, and any excess of force. Play octaves only for short periods of time, alternating them with scales and other finger exercises. The practice of technic should occupy one-third of the daily practice period.

TECHNICAL EXERCISES

For developing a comprehensive technic for advanced piano playing

Compiled by Charles Dennee

XVII
(pp f) (f pp)
(f pp) (pp f)
(pp f) (f pp)
(f pp) (pp f)
XVIII
mf
XIX
mf
XX
XXI
XXII
XXIII
XXIV
etc.
XXV
etc.
XXVI
XXVII
XXVIII
XXIX
XXX
XXXI

THE WEDGE
A
simile
continue
continue
B
continue
continue
C
continue
continue
D
continue
continue
THE TURN
DENNÉE
simile
simile
etc.

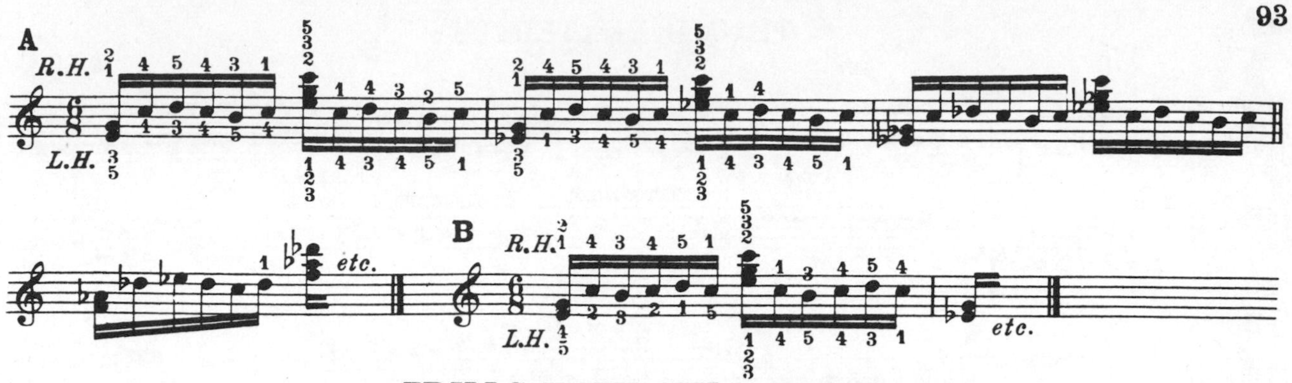

A

R.H.

L.H.

etc.

B

R.H.

L.H.

etc.

TRILLS WITH HELD TONES

TAUSIG

etc.

E PISCHNA

continue

Finger Independence

TAUSIG

continue

continue

continue

continue

THUMB DEXTERITY

PISCHNA

Exercises with Held Tones, for finger Independence.
Avoid overtaxing the muscles in playing the held tones. Attack the broken octaves with a strong thumb and finger stroke. Hold each tone to its full value.

PISCHNA

ff

APPEGGIO PASSAGES WITH DOUBLE NOTES
C. TAUSIG
A
etc.
B
etc.
STUDY
C. TAUSIG
Allegro
f
BROKEN CHORD PASSAGES WITH OCTAVES
C. TAUSIG
etc.

TAUSIG
I r. h.
l. h.
etc.
II r. h.
l. h.
etc.
III r. h.
l. h.
etc.
IV r. h.
l. h.
etc.
DOUBLE THIRDS
PISCHNA
A
etc.
B
etc.

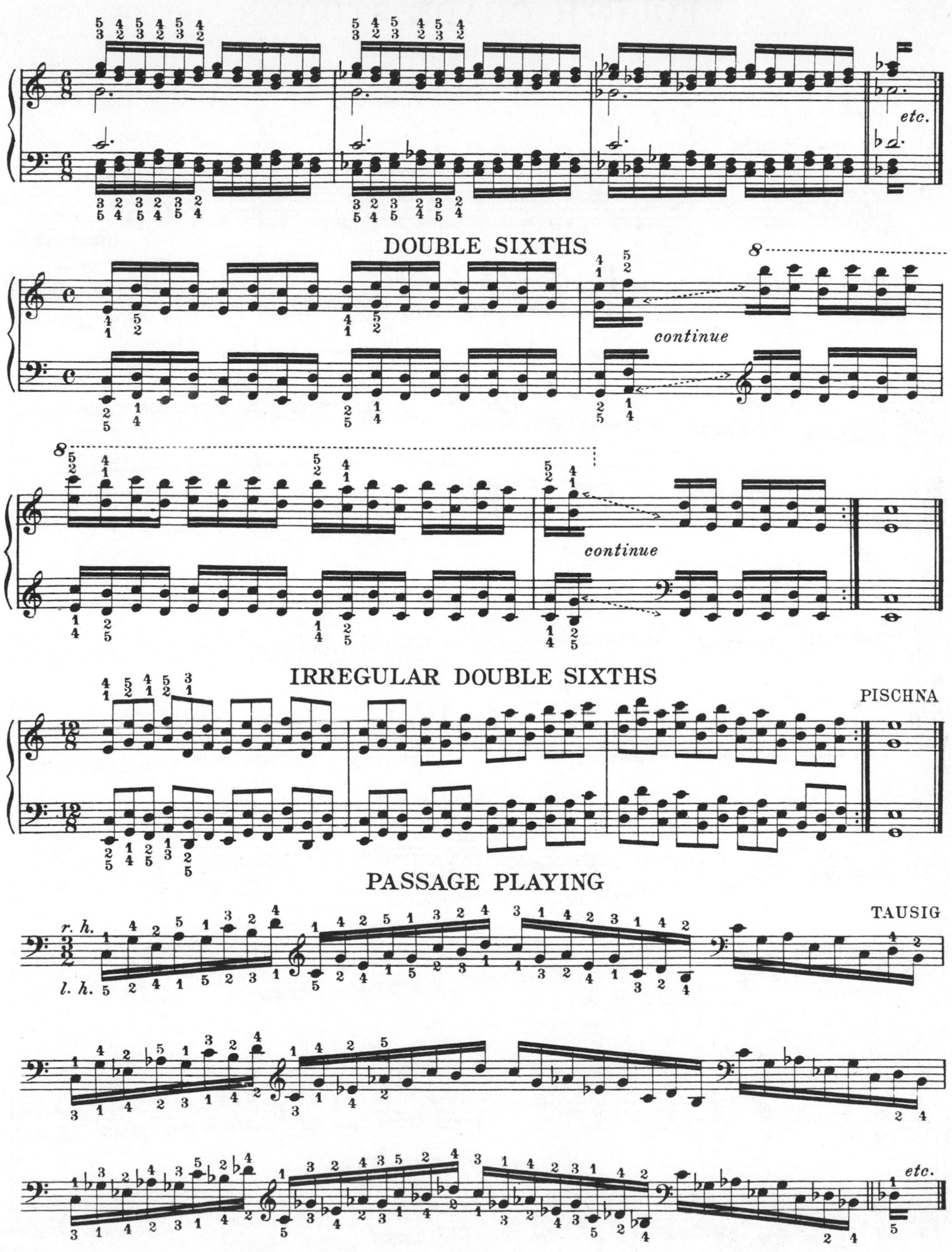
DOUBLE SIXTHS
continue
IRREGULAR DOUBLE SIXTHS
PISCHNA
PASSAGE PLAYING
TAUSIG
r. h.
l. h.
etc.

FOURTH GRADE STUDIES

STUDY

No. I, C Major

cresc.
f
ten.
fz
dimin.
p
più p
pp

STUDY IN A MAJOR

J. B. CRAMER

sempre cresc.
ten.

STUDY IN F-SHARP MINOR

CRAMER

Transpose to F minor

Transposing this study into G minor and F minor will increase its utility from a technical stand point.

STUDY
G MAJOR

Vivace (♩ = 116)

CZERNY

ff

staccato sempre

f

ff

STUDY
A-FLAT

CZERNY

STUDY IN F MINOR

CRAMER

Allegro non troppo (𝅗𝅥. = 72)

Transpose this study to F♯ minor

cres - cen - do

ten.

ff

sfz

STUDY
E MAJOR

ALOYS SCHMITT
Op.16, № 17

cresc.
dim.
p
p
cresc.
cresc.
f

STUDY
A MINOR

ALOYS SCHMITT

1.
2.
p
dim.
p
p
cresc.
dim.

pp
cresc.
f

dim.
sf
f
dim.
p
f

p
cresc.
f

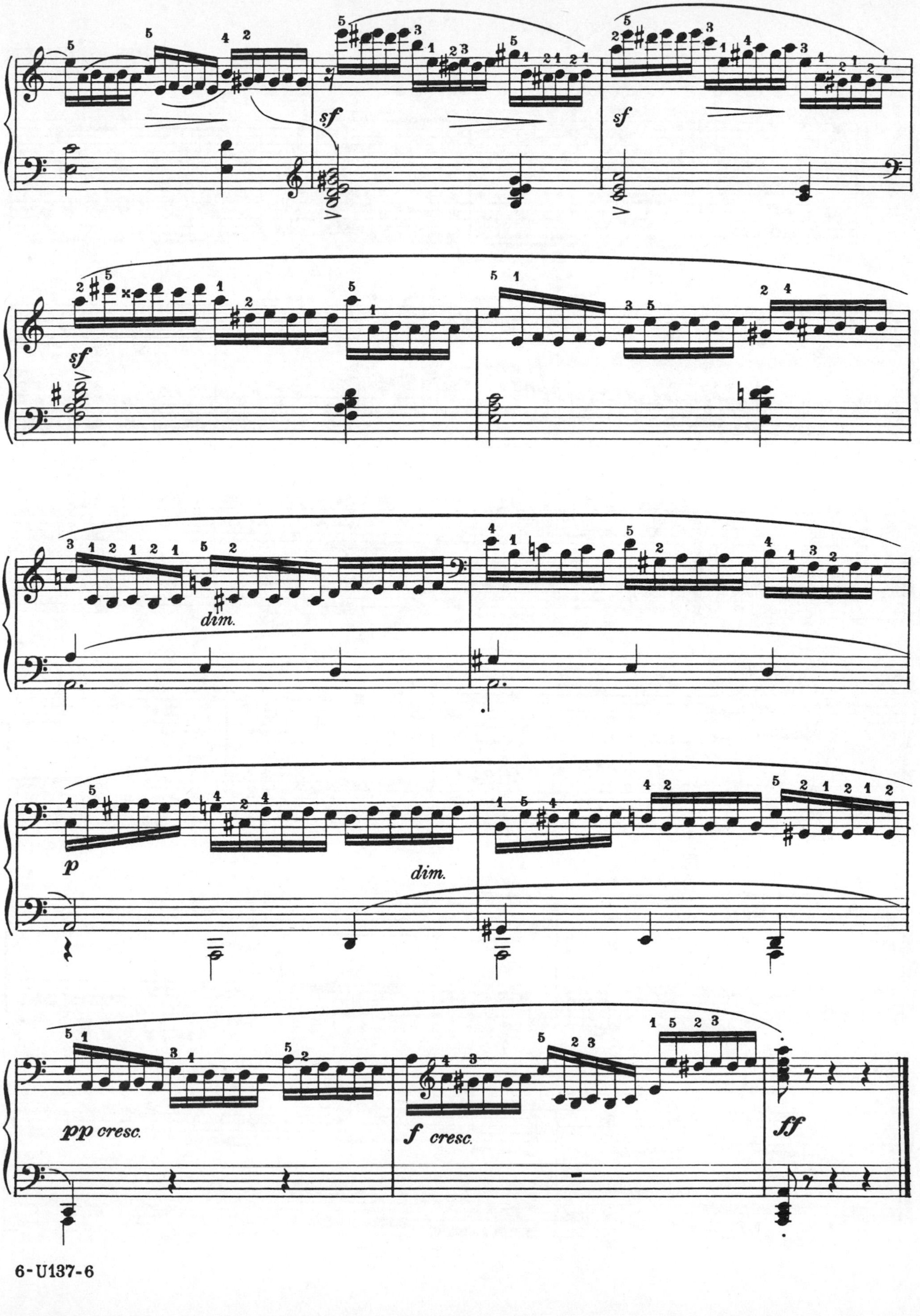
sf
sf
sf
sf
dim.
p
dim.
pp cresc.
f cresc.
ff

STUDY

E-FLAT MAJOR

ALOYS SCHMITT
Op. 16, Nº 16

p
pp legato
molto cresc.
ff

STUDY

ALOYS SCHMITT
Op.16, No. 2

sempre legato

f
con espressione
fp
staccato e marcato
rit.
Più lento

Tempo I.
Ped.
con espressione
dim.
sf
f
pp

STUDY
G MAJOR, No. IX

CRAMER

sfz
p
cresc.
dim.
p
mf
tr
dim.
p
cresc.
tr
f
p
mf
p
cresc.
sfz
mf

STUDY

C MAJOR, No. XXXI

Allegro con molto brio

CLEMENTI

ten.
fz
ten.
ten.
fz
ten.
fz
fz
fz
f
fz
ten.
fz

8
ff
mf
cresc.
f
ff
ten.
fz
ten.
ten.
fz
fz
ten.
fz
ten.
fz
ten.
fz

ten.
fz
ten.
fz
fz
fz
fz
fz

fz
8
dim.
f
ten.
8
più f
ten.
ten.
ff
fz
fz
fz
dim.
p
f

STUDY

F MAJOR, No. LXVIII

CRAMER

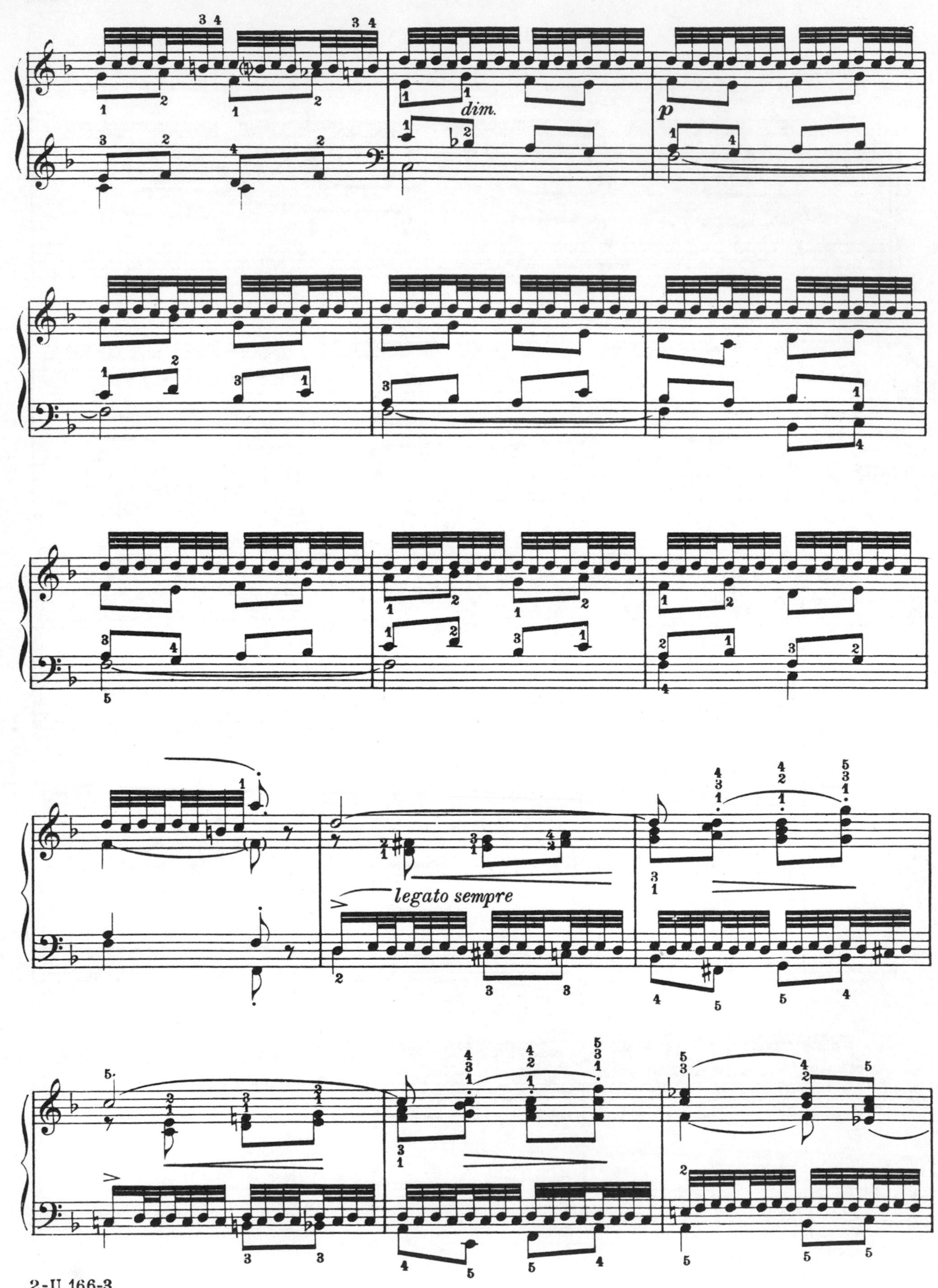
dim.
p
legato sempre

legato sempre

STUDY

A MINOR

CRAMER

dim.
dolce
f
dim.
p
p
smorzando

INVENTION

TWO-VOICE, No.IV, D MINOR

J. S. BACH

cresc.
fr
f
mf
cresc.
f

TWO-VOICE INVENTION

B-FLAT MAJOR, No. XIV

BACH

Andante con moto

cresc.
p
p
p
p
mf
mf

TWO-VOICE INVENTION

B MINOR, No. XV

BACH

p
f slargando

TWO-VOICE INVENTION

F MINOR, No. IX

p
cresc.
f
dim.
tr

STUDY
D MINOR, No. XVIII

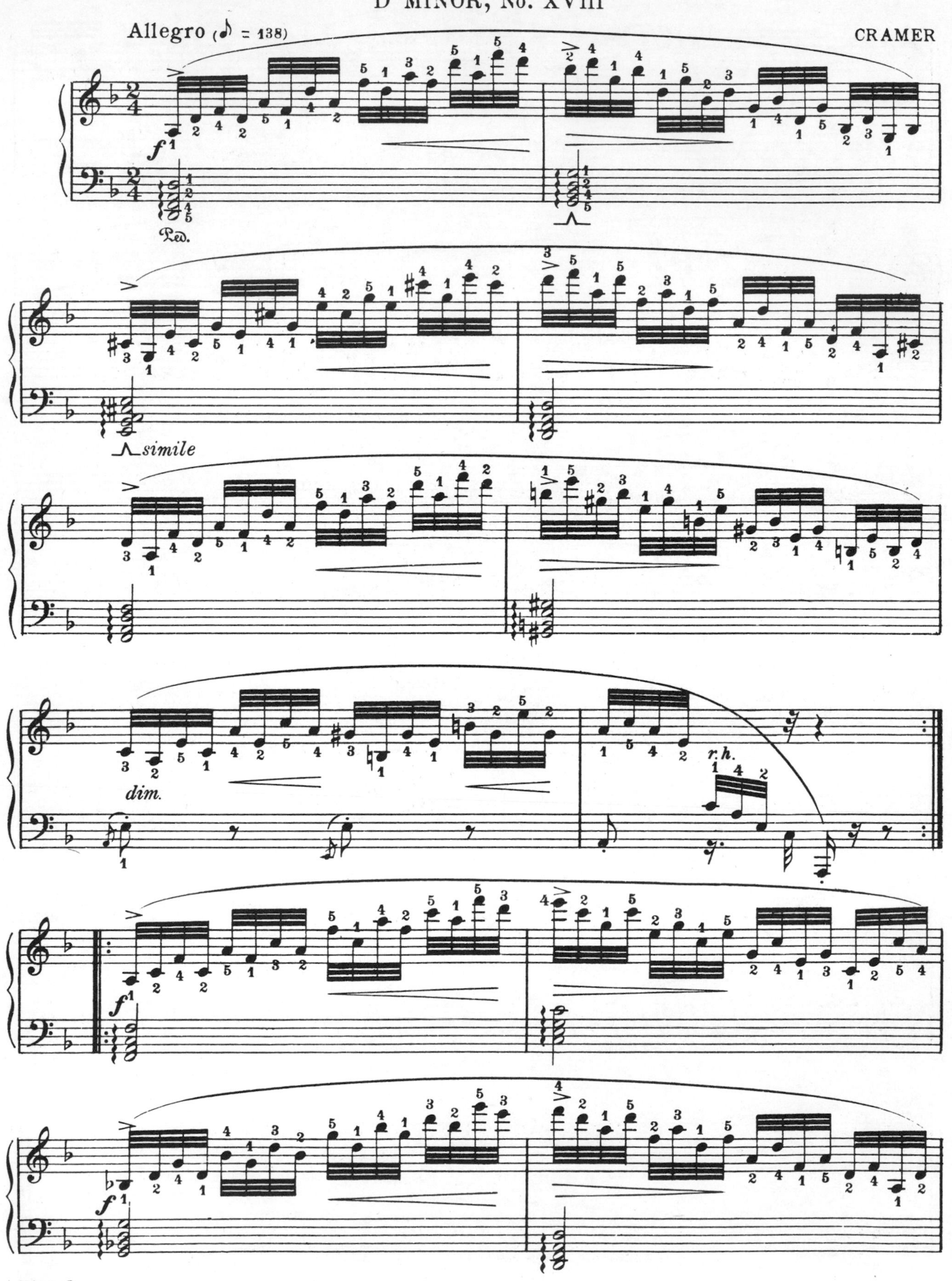

f
staccato
senza Ped.
dim.
p

STUDY

D MAJOR, No. LVI

CRAMER

cresc.
f
dim.
p
cresc.
f
Ped.
ten.
f
Ped.
Ped.
Ped.
Ped.

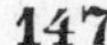

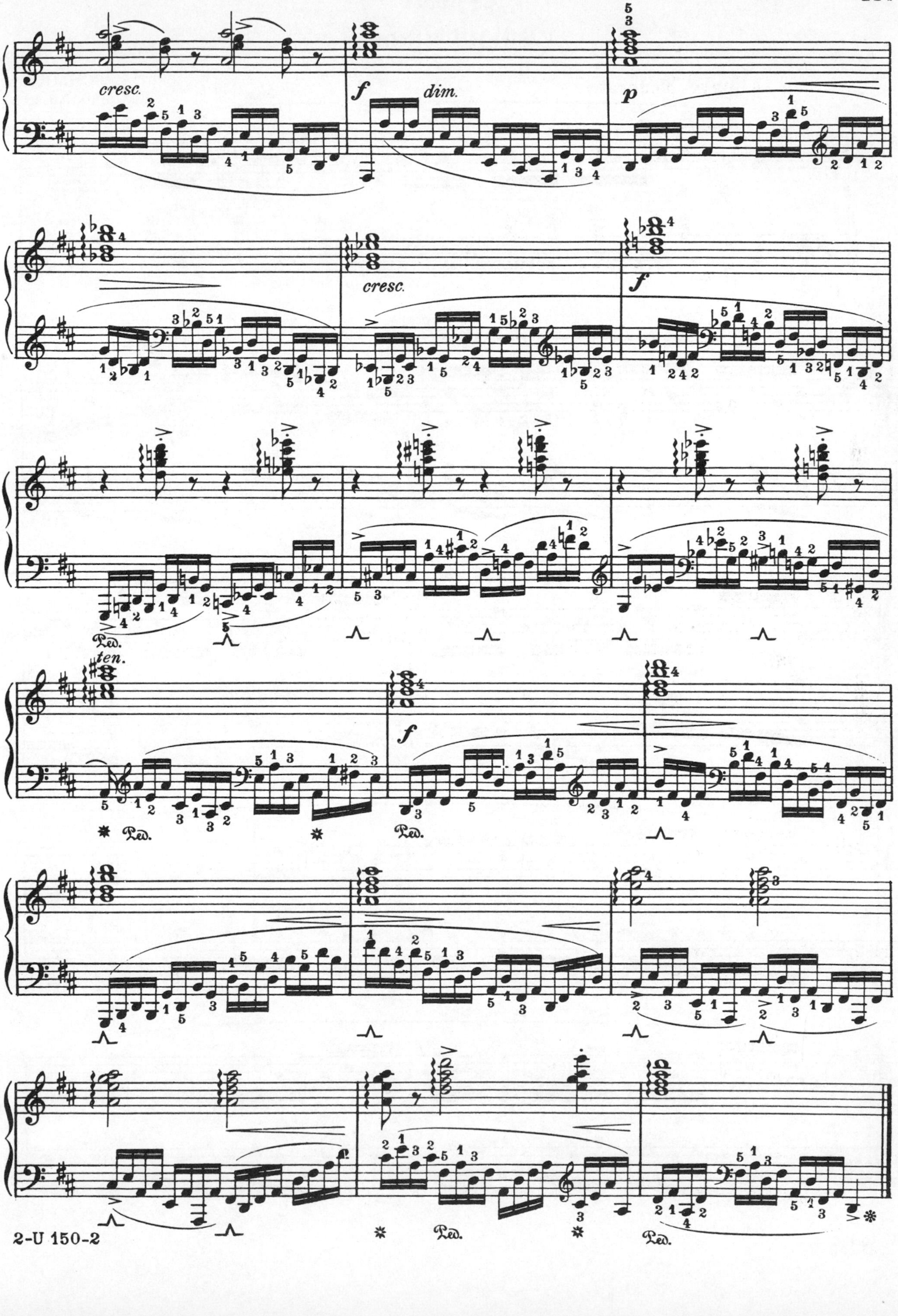

STUDY
F-SHARP MINOR

A. SCHMITT
Op. 16, No. 10

ten.
ten
ten
ten
ten
ten
ten
ten
ten
ten
ten
ten
ten.

legato
ff
sf
f
ff risoluto

stacc.
ten.
ten.
ten.
ten.
fz
ff
ten.

STUDY

E MINOR

CRAMER

dim.
p
mf
f

STUDY IN C MAJOR

CRAMER

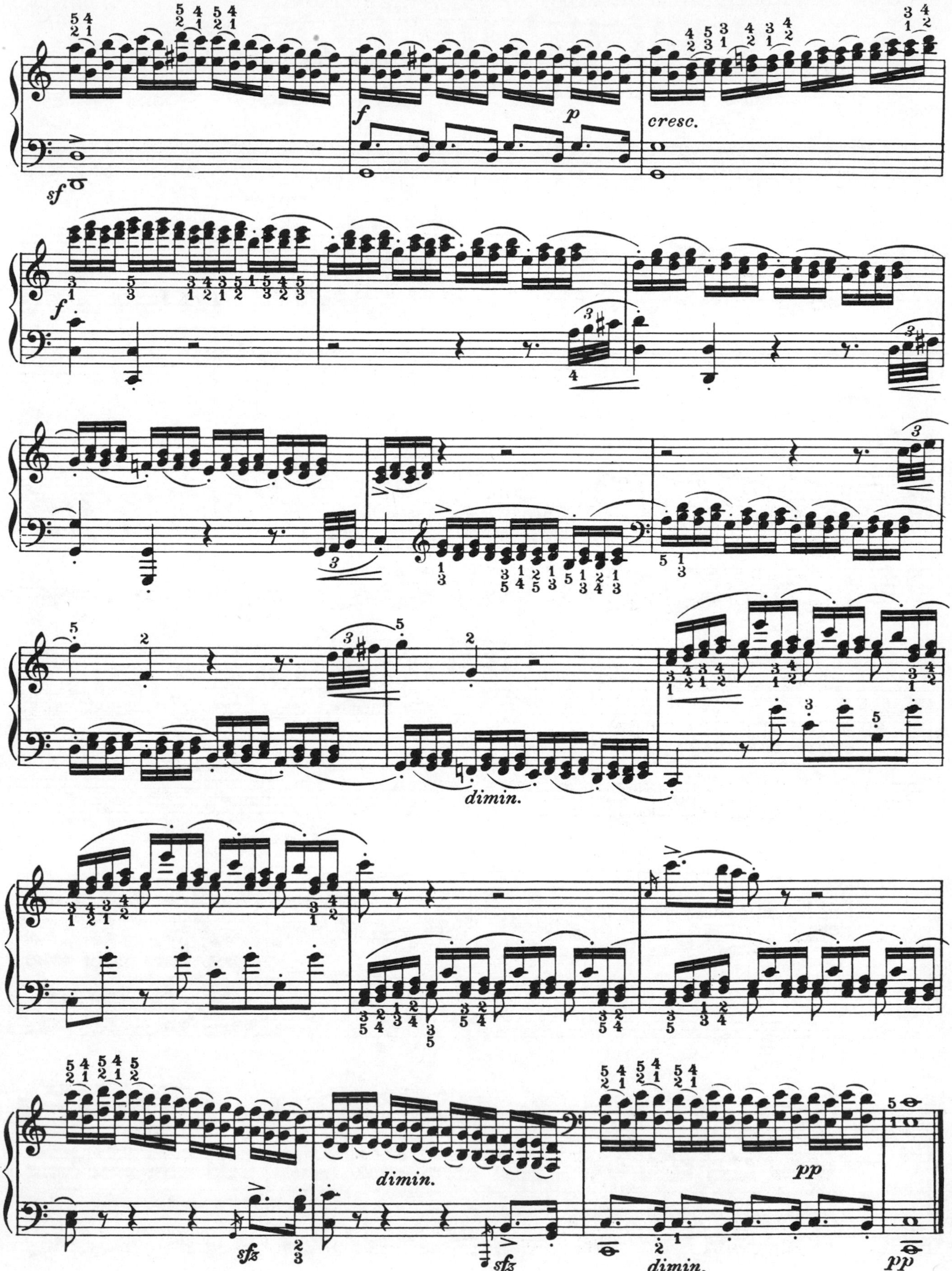
cresc.
dimin.
dimin.
dimin.

Allegro strepitoso (𝅗𝅥 = 120 - 144) STUDY IN D MINOR

CRAMER

cre - scen - do
simile
sempre f
ten.
(dimin)

EXERCISE

CZERNY

EXERCISE
G MAJOR

CZERNY

STUDY
B-FLAT MAJOR, No. XXXVII

Prestissimo (♩= 76) CRAMER

f
f
cresc.
dim.
f
cresc.
dim.
dolce
dim.
p

STUDY

D MINOR, No. XXXII

CRAMER

cresc.
f
p

cresc.
f
dim.
tr
dim.
pp

STUDY

CZERNY
Op. 740, No. 37

f
sf
fz
sf
sf
sf
sf
sf
ff

dim.
p leggiero
cresc.
f
sf
dim.
p
1
2
cresc.
p

Molto Allegro (𝅗𝅥 = 88) STUDY IN F MAJOR CZERNY. Op. 740

dim.
p
p
f
dim.
p
cresc.
f
Ped.
Ped.

p
cresc.
f
sf
Ped.
fp
legato
leggiermente
cresc.
fp
cresc.
f
cresc.
ff

STUDY, C MAJOR

For dexterity in expanded second finger crossing

A. SCHMITT
Op. 16, No. 4

STUDY

C MAJOR, No. XCV

CLEMENTI

Vivace con bizzarria

fz
dim.
p
f
dim.
p
staccato il basso

cresc.
l.h.
p
fz
fz
fz
fz
p
cresc.
f

p
cresc.
f
ff
fz
rall.
a tempo
p
staccato il basso
l.h. cresc.
f

STUDY
E FLAT MAJOR

CZERNY
Op. 740, No. 5

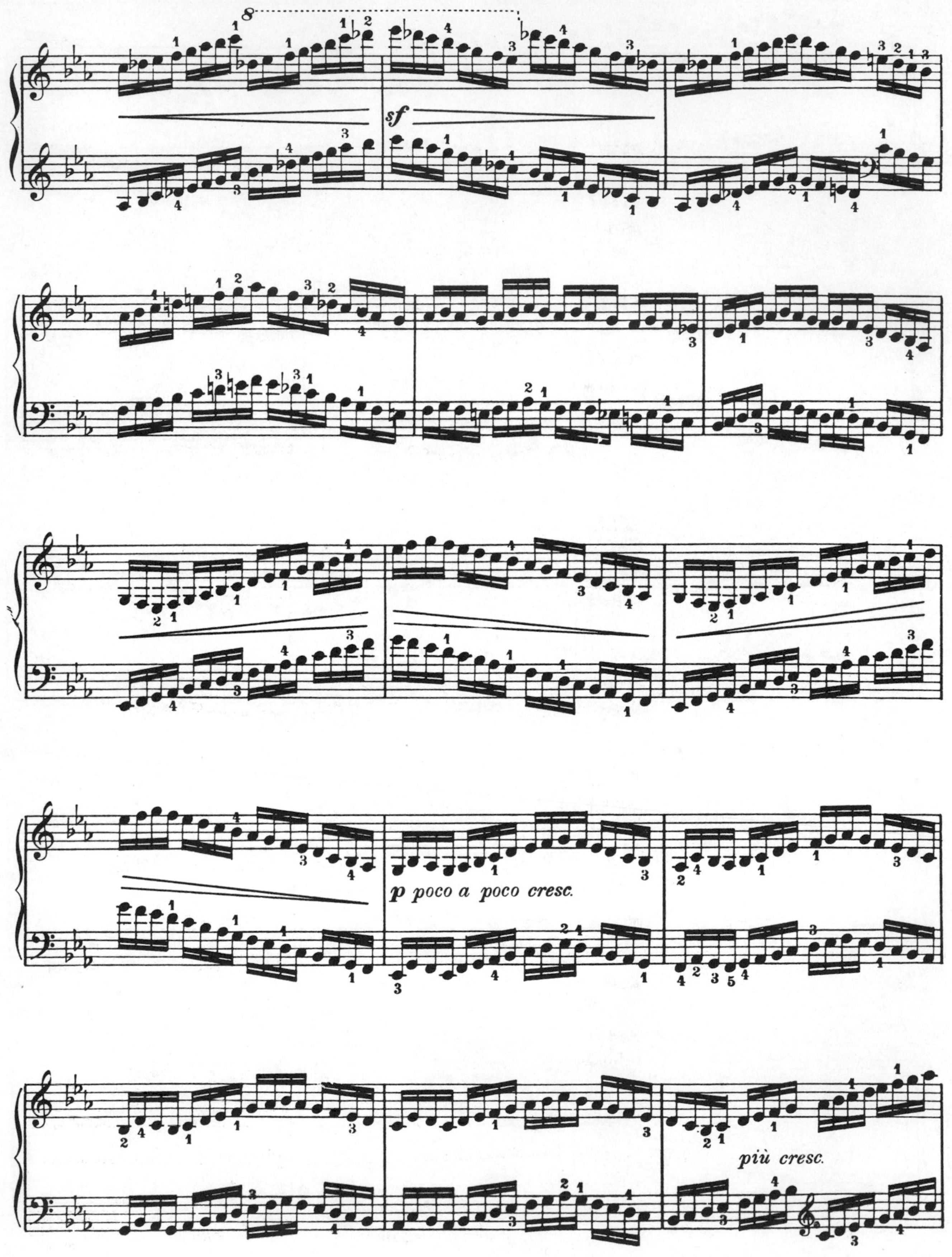
sf
p poco a poco cresc.
più cresc.

f
sf
sf
sf
sf
più f
sf
ff
fz
sf

STUDY
A MINOR

CZERNY
Op. 740. No. 41

fz
cresc.
ff
sempre ff
Ped.

STUDY IN D MAJOR

To be played with the utmost distinctness, but smoothness, of touch; strict observance of accent, shading and contrasts is imperative.

leggiero
leggiero
leggiero
leggiero

STUDY
C MAJOR, No. XVI

CLEMENTI

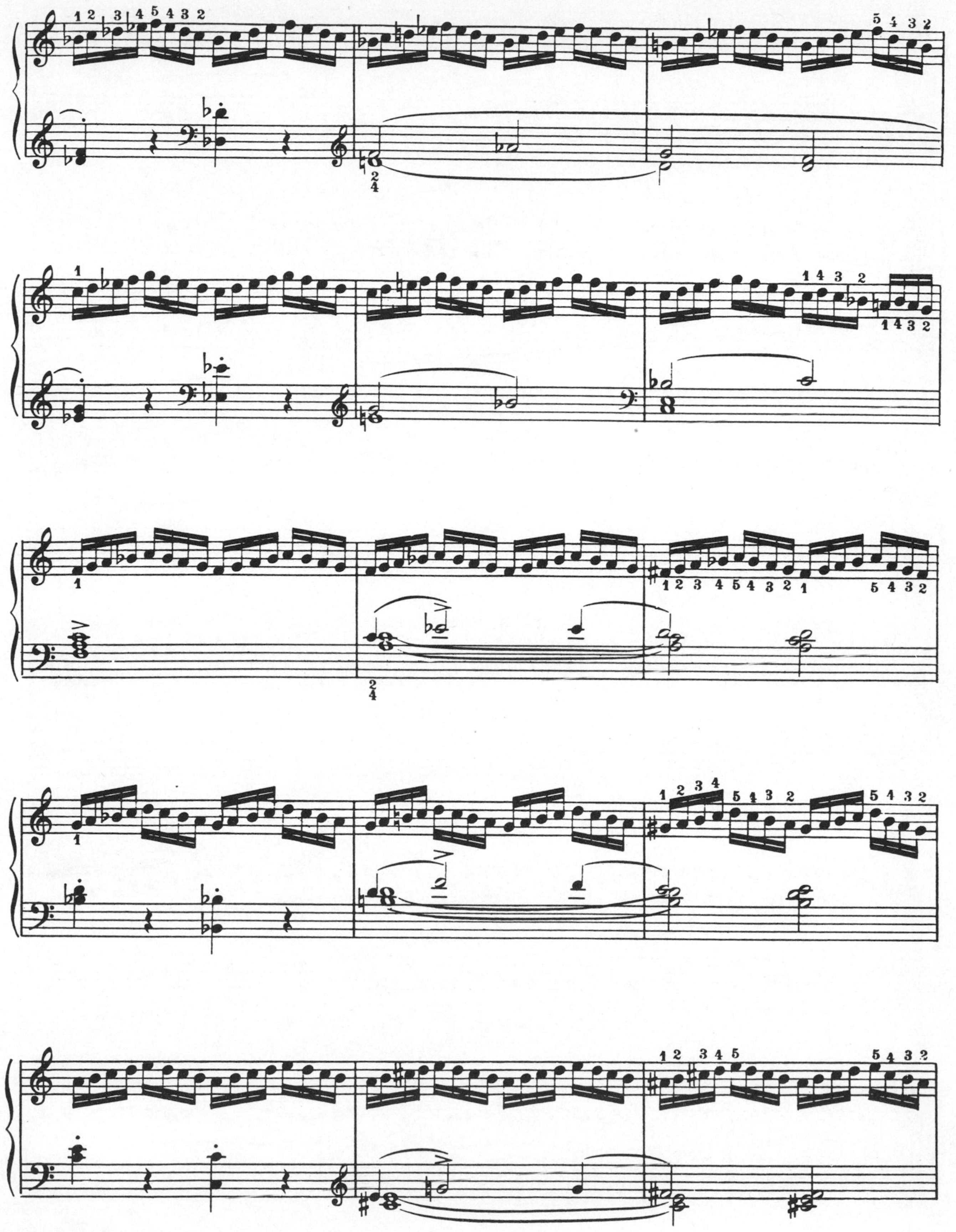

Edited by
CHARLES DENNÉE

STUDY IN A MINOR

CZERNY, Op. 740, № 31

Practise with firmness and precision at first; ultimately play with a light, free finger touch, using extreme care in the observance of light and shade as indicated by the marking.

f
sf
p
leggiero
dolce
8
f
fz
ff
p

f
Ped.
ff
fz

STUDY

C MAJOR, No. XVII

CLEMENTI

U 179-3

cresc.

THREE-VOICE INVENTION

D MINOR, No. IV

Allegretto moderato (♩ = 84) BACH

dim.
cresc.
cresc.
cresc.
dim. poco a poco

THREE-VOICE INVENTION
E MAJOR, No. VI

BACH

p
f
dim.
p
cresc.
f
f
dim. e poco rit.
p

STUDY
G MAJOR, No. LXXVIII

CLEMENTI

8
fz
legato

ff
fz
fz
fz
fz
dim.
p
f

STUDY

F MINOR, No. XLIV

CLEMENTI

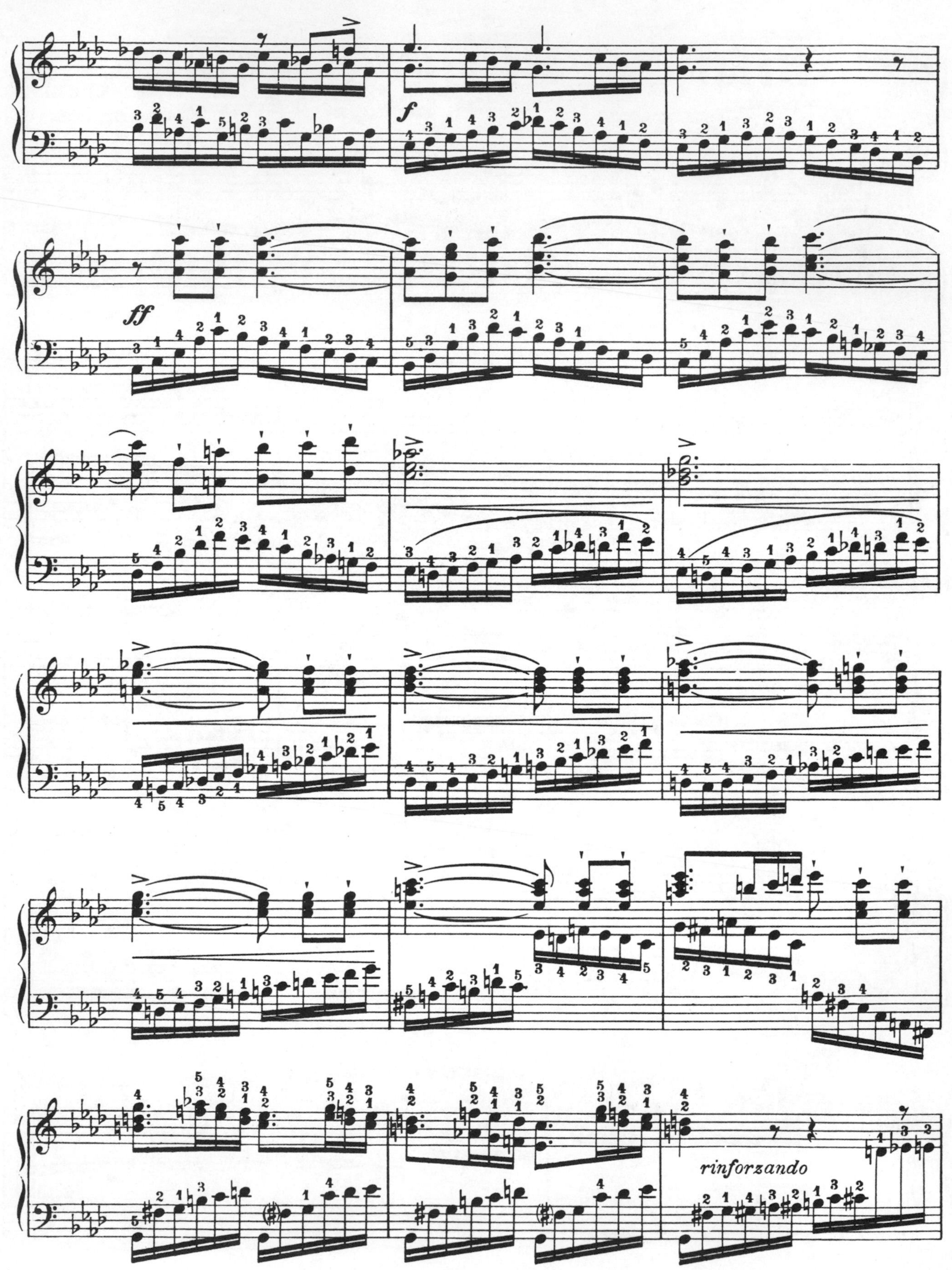
f
ff
rinforzando

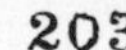

ff *p* *cresc.* *f* *più f* *ff* *ff* *fz* *fz*

ten.
ten.
ten.
p
cresc.

8
8
f
ff

rinforzando
ff
p
cresc.
f
più f

rinforzando
ff
rinforzando sempre
fz
fz
fz
fz

STUDY MATERIAL

GRADES I to IV

General Index

COMPOSERS IN ALPHABETICAL ORDER

	Vol.	Page
A		
Ascher, J.		
A Simple Story	I	83
B		
Bach, Johann Sebastian		
Invention, Two Voice, *C major*, No. I	II	72
Invention, Two Voice, *D minor*, No. IV	II	136
Invention, Two Voice, *F major*, No. VIII	II	73
Invention, Two Voice, *F minor*, No. IX	II	142
Invention, Two Voice, *B-flat*, No. XIV	II	138
Invention, Two Voice, *B minor*, No. XV	II	140
Invention, Three Voice, *D minor*, No. IV	II	194
Invention, Three Voice, *E major*, No. VI	II	196
Prelude, *C minor*	II	16
Prelude, *F major*	II	15
Song, from Anna Magdalene's Notebook	I	112
Bartok, Bela		
"Off Side" a Study in Phrasing	I	108
Etude	II	83
Berens, Hermann (*Bare-ens*)		
Hippety-Hop, Op. 70	I	51
Lightly Tripping Along, Op. 70	I	67
Study, *C major*, Op. 61, No. 1	II	40
Study, *C major*, Op. 61, No. 5	II	44
Study, *C major*, Op. 61, No. 9	II	46
Study, *C major*, Op. 61, No. 11	II	48
Study, *C major*, Op. 70, No. 34	I	153
Study, *C major*, Op. 70, No. 44	I	162
Study, *F major*, Op. 70, No. 50	I	160
Study, *C major*, Op. 79, No. 15	I	193
Study, *C major*, Op. 79, No. 16	I	192
Study, *C major*, Op. 79, No. 19	I	171
Study, *C major*, Op. 79, No. 20	I	172
Bertini, Henri Jerome (*Bare-tee-nee*)		
Prelude, Op. 100, No. 3	I	201
Study, *C major*	II	76
Study, *C major*	II	82
Study, *G minor*, Op. 29, No. 3	II	39
Study, *C minor*, Op. 29, No. 6	II	38
Study. *C minor*, Op. 29, No. 7	II	14
Study, *A minor*, Op. 29, No. 18	II	36
Study, *C major*, Op. 29, No. 22	II	49
Beyer, Ferdinand (*Buy-er*)		
Clown and Pantaloon	I	128
Early Morn	I	84
Rain is Falling, The (four hands)	I	44
Round We Go	I	41
Three Flour Hand Pieces; Homeward Bound, Slow Waltz, Primary School March	I	18
Whistling Farmer Boy, The	I	42

COMPOSERS IN ALPHABETICAL ORDER

	Vol.	Page
Burgmüller, Johann Friedrich (*Boorg-mee-ler*)		
Study, *G major*, Op. 100, No. 21	I	157
C		
Clementi, Muzio		
Allegretto, Op. 36	I	200
Shepherd's Pipe, from Sonatina, Op. 36, No. 3	I	130
Study, *C major*, No. XVI	II	184
Study, *C major*, No. XVIII	II	191
Study, *C major*, No. XXXI	II	126
Study, *F minor*, No. XLIV	II	201
Study, *G major*, No. LXXVII	II	198
Study, *C major*, No. XCV	II	172
Concone, Giuseppe (*Kon-kó-ne*)		
Study, *C major*, Op. 24, No. 24	I	166
Cramer, Johann Baptist (*Krah-mer*)		
Study, *C major*, No. I	II	100
Study, *G major*, No. IX	II	124
Study, *A minor*, No. XII	II	134
Study, *A major*, No. XIII	II	102
Study, *D minor*, No. XVIII	II	144
Study, *F-sharp minor*, No. XXII	II	104
Study, *D minor*, XXXII	II	162
Study, *B-flat*, No. XXXVII	II	160
Study, *F minor*, No. LI	II	108
Study, *C major*, No. LIV	II	154
Study, *D major*, No. LVI	II	146
Study, *E minor*, No. LXV	II	152
Study, *F major*, No. LXVIII	II	131
Study, *D minor*, No. LXIX	II	156
Czerny, Carl (*Chair-nee*)		
Exercise, *D major*	II	158
Exercise, *G major*	II	159
March, *C major*	I	202
Mazurka	I	107
Octave Studies	II	85
Study, *C major*, Op. 139, No. 19	I	174
Study, *D major*, Op. 139, No. 24	I	184
Study, *G major*, Op. 139, No. 25	I	194
Study, *D major*, Op. 139, No. 42	I	151
Study, *B-flat*, Op. 139, No. 45	I	174
Study, *C major*, Op. 139, No. 53	I	188
Study, *C major*, Op. 139, No. 61	I	165
Study, *C major*, Op. 299, No. 2	II	41
Study, *C major*, Op. 299, No. 3	II	26
Study, *C major*, Op. 299, No. 4	II	28
Study, *C major*, Op. 299, No. 6	II	30
Study, *C major*, Op. 299, No. 7	II	58

COMPOSERS IN ALPHABETICAL ORDER

	Vol.	Page
Study, *C major*, Op. 299, No. 11	II	32
Study, *F major*, Op. 299, No. 12	II	64
Study, *C major*, Op. 299, No. 18	II	34
Study, *E-flat*, Op. 299, No. 25	II	68
Study, *C major*, Op. 299, No. 32	II	70
Study, *G major*, Op. 599, No. 18	I	164
Study, *G major*, Op. 599, No. 59	I	197
Study, *F major*, Op. 599, No. 87	I	196
Study, *E-flat*, Op. 636, No. 12	II	57
Study, *G major*, Op. 718, No. 5	I	198
Study, *F major*, Op. 740	II	168
Study, *E-flat*, Op. 740, No. 5	II	176
Study, *D major*, Op. 740, No. 21	II	182
Study, *A minor*, Op. 740, No. 31	II	188
Study, *D minor*, Op. 740, No. 37	II	165
Study, *A minor*, Op. 740, No. 41	II	180
Study, *F major*, Op. 777, No. 20	I	195
Study, *C major*, Op. 777, No. 21	I	161
Study, *D major*, Op. 821, No. 22	I	184
Study, *E major*, Op. 821, No. 33	II	43
Study, *E major*, Op. 821, No. 35	II	43
Study, *B major*, Op. 821, No. 43	II	44
Study, *B-flat minor*, Op. 821, No. 76	II	65
Study, *C major*, Op. 821, No. 107	II	61
Study, *C major*, Op. 821, No. 108	II	61
Study, Op. 740, No. 49	II	106
Study, *G major*	I	198
Study, *F major*	I	204
Study, *B-flat*	II	22
Study, *D major*	II	79
Study, *G major*	II	80
Study, *A-flat*	II	107
Waltz, *C major*	I	107

D

	Vol.	Page
Dennée, Charles Frederick		
Country Boy's Song	I	25
Dance of the Clowns	I	79
Dolly's Polka	I	127
Good Resolve, A	I	16
Hands Go Traveling, The	I	50
Left Hand Imitates the Right	I	17
Little Recreations in Note Values	I	21
Little Song	I	25
Merry Roundelay, A	I	25
My First Waltz	I	17
Plaintive Mood	I	25
Study in Motion	I	113
Two Short Studies in Rolled Chords	I	104
Up the Ladder and Down the Ladder	I	39
Duvernoy, Jean B. (*Du-vairn-wah*)		
Study, Op. 120, No. 5 (Adapted from)	II	12
Study, *C major*, Op. 120, No. 7	I	189
Study, *C major*, Op. 120, No. 8	II	53
Study, *C major*, Op. 176, No. 4	I	147
Study, *D major*, Op. 176, No. 9	I	168
Study, *C major*, Op. 176, No. 13	I	167
Study, *C major*, Op. 176, No. 23	I	167
Study, *C major*	I	191
Study, *G major*	I	190

COMPOSERS IN ALPHABETICAL ORDER

E

	Vol.	Page
Ehmant, A (*Ay mont*)		
Theme and Variations	I	76

F

	Vol.	Page
Foster, Stephen		
Old Black Joe	I	34
Fredric, C.		
Agile Fingers	I	80
Dolly's First Waltz	I	41
Fairy March	I	26
Graceful Dance	I	26
Little Song, A	I	47
Morning Song	I	87
Round Dance	I	86
Skating	I	121
Traveling Through the Keys	I	99

G

	Vol.	Page
Gray, Th.		
And He Said	I	112
Gurlitt, Cornelius (*Goor-lit*)		
Conversation, A, Op. 82, No. 44	I	85
Study, Op. 82, No. 34	I	130
Study, First Velocity, Op. 83, No. 1	I	69
Study, Second Velocity, Op. 83, No. 2	I	77
Study, Third Velocity, Op. 83, No. 3	I	101
Study, Fourth Velocity, Op. 83, No. 4	I	102
Study, Fifth Velocity, Op. 83, No. 5	I	125
Study, Sixth Velocity, Op. 83, No. 6	I	126
Study, *C major*, Op. 83, No. 13	I	154
Study, *C major*, Op. 83, No. 14	I	155
Study, *G major*, Op. 83, No. 15	I	178
Study, *G major*, Op. 83, No. 16	I	179
Study, *C major*, Op. 83, No. 19	I	158
Study, *C major*, Op. 83, No. 20	I	159

H

	Vol.	Page
Hasert, Rudolph (*Hah-zert*)		
Study, *E minor*, Op. 50, No. 11	II	62
Heller, Stephen (*Hell-air*)		
On the Train	I	206
Study, *A minor*, Op. 45, No. 2	II	42
Study, *D minor*, Op. 54, No. 15	II	60
Study, *B-flat*, Op. 45, No. 16	II	50
Hummel, Johann Nepomuk		
Theme and Variations	I	23

K

	Vol.	Page
Köhler, Louis (*Kay-ler*)		
Country Dance, *G major*	I	111
Cuckoo, The	I	85
Etude Joyeuse, *C major*	I	203
Rose Garden, A	I	79

COMPOSERS IN ALPHABETICAL ORDER

	Vol.	Page
Studies, Scale, Op. 151, No. 9	I	131
Study, *C major*, Op. 50, No. 3	I	180
Study, *C major*, Op. 50, No. 4	I	181
Study, *C major*, Op. 50, No. 9	I	163
Study, *C major*, Op. 50, No. 10	I	163
Study, *C major*, Op. 60, No. 2	I	182
Study, *C major*, Op. 151, No. 1	I	148
Study, *C major*, Op. 151, No. 2	I	149
Study, *C major*, Op. 157, No. 3	I	146
Study, *C major*, Op. 157, No. 8	I	177
Study, *C major*, Op. 157, No. 11	I	168
Study, *C major*, Op. 242, No. 10	I	185

Kullak, Theodore (*Koo-lak*)

Theme and Variations	I	90

Le Couppey, Felix (*Leh-koop-pay*)

Study, *G major*, Op. 20, No. 4	II	13
Study, *B-flat*, Op. 20, No. 13	II	37

L

Lemoine, Henri (*Lem-wahn*)

Mill, The	I	115
Study, *G major*	II	54
Study, *G major*	II	20
Study, *C major*	II	24
Study, *C major*, Op. 37, No. 1	I	156
Study, *C major*, Op. 37, No. 2	I	156
Study, *G major*, Op. 37, No. 8	I	169
Study, *A minor*, Op. 37, No. 10	I	170
Study, *F major*, Op. 37, No. 20	I	173
Study, *G major*, Op. 37, No. 49	II	56

Loeschhorn, Albert (*Lesh-horn*)

Basket, Full, A	I	51
Down in the Meadow the Grass is so Green	I	95
Kittens Playing	I	95
Study, *C minor*, Op. 38, No. 23	II	66
Study, *C major*, Op. 65, No. 4	I	152
Study, *A major*, Op. 65, No. 46	I	199
Study, *A minor*, Op. 66, No. 8	I	182
Study in Elementary Expansion	I	47
Study in Expansion	I	74

M

Müller, August Eberhardt (*Mee-ler*)

Theme and Variations	I	31

P

Pasconet, J. N.

Parade of the Boy Scouts	I	89

S

Schmitt, Aloys

Five Finger Exercises, Progressive, from Op. 16	II	1
Five Finger Figures in varied groupings, from Op. 16	I	133
Study, *C major*	II	78
Study, *G major*	II	84
Study, *E major*	II	110
Study, *A minor*	II	112
Study, *B-flat*	II	118
Study, *E-flat*	II	120
Study, *F-sharp minor*	II	148
Study, *C major*, Op. 16, No. 4	II	171
Study, *C major*, Op. 16, No. 8	II	52
Study, *E-flat*, Op. 16, No. 24	II	74

Schumann, Robert (*Shoo-mahn*)

Study, *G major*, Op. 68, No. 14	I	186

W

Wohlfahrt, Heinrich (*Vole-fart*)

Learning to Run	I	121
Little Dialogue, A	I	81
Study, Staccato Broken Triad Figures	I	114
Twelve Easy Pieces Without Key Signatures	I	58
Two Little Voices	I	108

Composers Not Listed

America	I	92
Answering Echoes	I	39
Answering Voices	I	22
Antiphonal, The First	I	53
Antiphonal, The Second	I	53
At the Circus	I	67
Baby's Lullaby	I	93
Bassoon Solo, A	I	30
Beginning on a Count other than "One"	I	56
Boys Sing an Old Favorite, The	I	94
Brook, The	I	124
Campbells Are Coming, The	I	57
Changing the Key—Modulation	I	35
Childhood Hymn, A	I	92
Children's Ball	I	122
Chords and Arpeggios	II	8
Contraction of Held Tones and Staccato	I	75
Consecutive Successions of Double Thirds	I	137
Daily Round, The	I	24
Dancing in a Foreign Land	I	50
Definitions, Practical, of Musical Terms	I	142
Diatonic Finger Passages and Simple Broken Triads	I	46
Dutch Dance	I	127
Elementary Key Analysis	I	36
Elements of Music	I	1
Embellishments	I	143
Evening Barcarolle, An	I	50
Exercises for Finger Development and Control	I	9
Exercises in Moving Legato Double Notes	I	97
Figures Moving Around Held Keys	I	135
Finger Substitution	I	66
First Attempt at Speed	I	43
Five Fingers Take a Stroll	I	13
Flute Solo, A	I	30
Fundamental Broken Triads	I	88
Hand Contraction	I	68
Hands Make a Tour in A major, The	I	50
Hand Organ	I	100
Happy Song	I	49

STUDY MATERIAL

COMPOSERS IN ALPHABETICAL ORDER

	Vol.	Page
Harp Player, The	I	114
Homeward Bound	I	50
In a Canoe	I	71
In Graceful Curves	I	40
Juggler, The	I	96
Keyboard of a Modern Pianoforte	I	6
Keyboard Shifting	I	104
Left Hand Explores the Upper Region	I	21
Left Hand Gains Courage	I	22
Little Jack Horner	I	33
Little Lost Dog, The	I	34
Little Oboe and the Big Trombone, The	I	33
Little Puzzle	I	151
Little Studies Built on Slow Trills	I	11
London Bridge	I	33
Maypole Dance	I	31
Morning Recreation	I	24
Morning Salute	I	49
Musical Terms	I	132
Old Hymn Book, From an	I	94
Old Southern Song, An	I	93
Oral Accent or Impulse Training	I	32
Passing under of the Thumb and Crossing over of Fingers	II	2
Peasants' Polka	I	85
Pedals, The	I	132
Position at the Pianoforte	I	7
Practice of the Scale, The	I	118
Pussy Cat at Play	I	22
Recollections of Infant Days	I	65
Repeating a Key with the Same Finger	I	43
Rolled Triads	I	104
Rhythm	I	3
Scale Study	I	123
Scales, Major, in Double Thirds	II	10
Scales, Minor, in Double Thirds	II	11

COMPOSERS IN ALPHABETICAL ORDER

	Vol.	Page
Scales, The Easier Major	I	119
Scales and Cadences in all Major and Minor Keys	I	138
Scales and Staccato	I	129
Schöne Minka	I	82
Schumann's Rules for Young Musicians	I	8
Scotch Fife and Drum Corps Plays a Dance Tune, The	I	94
Shifting Keyboard Position	I	78
Signs and Abbreviations	I	132
Simple Accompaniment Models	I	72
Simple Broken Thirds	I	37
Simple Scales	I	116
Slow Dance	I	74
Song, A	I	65
Song of the Hussars	I	105
Song of the Toiler	I	24
Spinning Wheel, The	I	89
Staccato	I	55
Studies in Contrary and Parallel Motion	I	12
Study, *C major*	I	176
Study for Independence and Speed	I	122
Study in Broken Thirds	I	109
Study in Contrary Motion	I	17
Study in Double Notes	I	87
Study in Intervals	I	16
Study in Little Runs	I	83
Study in Staccato Sixths	I	111
Tagging	I	38
Taps	I	33
Tonic and Seventh Chord Arpeggios in all Keys	I	144
Twister, A	I	37
Two Little Canons	I	22
Up and Down the Piazza Steps	I	16
Varied Note Values and Intervals	I	46
Wooden Shoe Dance	I	64

LIST OF GRADE III AND IV COMPOSITIONS

CONTAINED IN THE INTERNATIONAL LIBRARY OF MUSIC

ARRANGED PROGRESSIVELY FROM THE EASIER TO THE MORE DIFFICULT.

GRADE III

Title	Composer	Vol.	Page
Norse Song, Op. 68, No. 14	Schumann	I	261
The Dove Côte	Ladoukhine	I	262
Bridal Chorus, from "Lohengrin"	Wagner	I	263
Remembrance, Op. 71, No. 7	Grieg	I	268
Dance Caprice, Op. 28, No. 3	Grieg	I	270
Barcarolle, from "Tales of Hoffman"	Offenbach	I	274
March of the Toy Soldiers	de Benedictis	I	277
Waltz Serenade	Poldini	I	280
Für Elise	Beethoven	I	282
Rondo, *G major*	Glière	I	286
Consolation, Op. 30, No. 3	Mendelssohn	I	288
Farewell to the Piano	Beethoven	I	290
In the Meadow	Lichner	I	294
Song without Words	Ladoukhine	I	298
Gavotte	Gossec	I	300
Toccatina	Maykapar	I	302
A Little Girl Rocking her Doll	Rebikoff	I	304
The Meadow at Eventide	Rebikoff	I	306
A Mother Beside the Cradle	Rebikoff	I	308
Skating Children	Rebikoff	I	310
Valse Mignonne	Rebikoff	I	312
Canzonetta, Op. 20, No. 9	Cui	I	316
Punch and Judy	Lemaire	I	318
Bluette (Polka)	Bachmann	I	320
Etude Joyeuse	Kopylow	I	327
Polonaise, from Sixth French Suite	Bach	I	332
Complaint	Korestchenko	I	333
Birds of Passage	Poldini	I	334
Gavotte	Martini	I	338
Cradle Song	Hauser	I	341
Serenade, Op. 32, No. 9	Jensen	I	344
Idylle	André	I	348
Melody in F	Rubinstein	II	353
The Birch Tree	Russian	II	357
A Story, Op. 21, No. 1	Karganoff	II	359
Concerto Theme	Tschaikowsky	II	362
Sinfonietta	Handel	II	364
Amaryllis	Louis XIII-Ghys.	II	366
Cantabile, Op. 20, No. 5	Cui	II	370
Danse Orientale	Lubomirsky	II	373
Prelude, Op. 28, No. 4	Chopin	II	374
Polonaise, Op. 93, No. 1	Spindler	II	376
Prelude and Fughetta	Armand	II	378
Tambourine (Rondo)	Rameau	II	380
Le Coucou (Rondo)	Daquin	II	382
The Flight of the Bumble Bee (Modified)	Rimsky-Korsakoff	II	388
Two Venetian Gondolas	Mendelssohn	II	394
Sarabanda	Handel	II	396
Little Romance, Op. 68, No. 26	Schumann	II	398
In the Mill	Rebikoff	II	400
La Cinquantaine	Gabriel-Marie	II	401
Thousand and One Nights	Strauss	II	404
Berceuse, from "Jocelyn"	Godard	II	413
Song without Words, No. XXII	Mendelssohn	II	416
Soldatini	Cantu	II	418
Song of Longing	Nicodé	II	420
Beside the Cradle, Op. 68, No. 5	Grieg	II	422
Prelude	Smetana	II	424
Rondo, Op. 11	Hummel	II	426
Elegy for a Sparrow	Lanciani	II	434
The Lonely Wanderer, Op. 43, No. 2	Grieg	II	436
Bagatelle	Beethoven	II	438
Chaconne, Op. 62	Durand	II	442
Kingdom Come	American	II	447
A Sketch	Sieveking	II	448
Largo, from "Xerxes"	Handel	II	450
Calinèrie	Ravina	II	453
Puck (Kobold)	Grieg	II	456
Humoresque	Pugno	II	459
Elevation	Flörsheim	II	462
Gavotte	Kopylow	II	464
Intermezzo, Op. 6, No. 4	Schumann	II	466
Cavalry March	Karganoff	II	468
Largo, from "New World" Symphony	Dvorak	II	470
Mazurka	Glière	II	472
Petite Valse, Op. 20, No. 3	Cui	II	474
Berceuse, Op. 20, No. 8	Cui	II	478
Souvenir Douloureux, Op. 20, No. 6	Cui	II	480
Elfin Dance, Op. 12, No. 4	Grieg	II	482
Birdling (Vöglein)	Grieg	II	484
Nocturne, *B-flat major*	Field	II	486
Barcarolle	Gade	II	489
The Mill, Op. 17, No. 3	Jensen	II	492
Minuetto, Op. 62, No. 5	P. Scharwenka	II	496
Mazurka, Op. 10, No. 3	Moszkowski	II	498
Prelude, Op. 28, No. 6	Chopin	II	500
Prelude, Op. 28, No. 7	Chopin	II	501
Valse Aerienne, Op. 148, No. 1	Spindler	II	502
Minuetto, *E-flat major*	Mozart	II	506
Watchman's Song, Op. 12, No. 3	Grieg	II	509

LIST OF GRADE III AND IV COMPOSITIONS

Title	Composer	Vol.	Page
Song of the Ploughman	Bachmann	II	510
Gypsy Rondo	Haydn	II	514
Six Variations, *G major*	Beethoven	II	520
Gavotte, from Fifth French Suite	Bach	II	527
Impromptu, Op. 142, No. 2	Schubert	II	528
Gavotte, from Sixth French Suite	Bach	II	531
Au Matin	Godard	II	532
Rondo	Dussek	II	536
Poupée Valsante	Poldini	II	539
By the Cradle	Jensen	II	544
Cabaletta	Lack	II	546
Romance	Raff	II	550
Funeral March, Op. 62, No. 3	Mendelssohn	II	554
Funeral March of a Marionette	Gounod	II	556
Norwegian Folk Dance, Op. 17, No. 1	Grieg	II	562
Nocturne, *E-flat major*	Field	II	564
Minuet, *C minor*	Bach	II	571
Andantino	Lemare	II	572
Song of India	Rimsky-Korsakoff	II	575
Legénde	Rebikoff	II	578
Barcarolle	Giuliani	II	580
Pierrot se-meurt	Oswald	II	582
Ring Dance	Gade	II	584
Cradle Song	Glière	II	586
A Moon Idyl, Op. 28, No. 3	MacDowell	II	588
A Flower Idyl, Op. 28, No. 1	MacDowell	II	594
A Flute Idyl, Op. 28, No. 5	MacDowell	II	591
Winter Time, Op. 68, No. 38	Schumann	II	597
Fughetta	Schumann	II	598
Mazurka, Op. 39, No. 10	Tschaikowsky	II	600
Dansa Misteriosa	Fernandez	II	602
Bluette	Froés	II	605
The Music Box	Liadow	II	608
By the Wayside (Suite)	Mortimer Wilson	II	612
Rustica (Suite)	Mortimer Wilson	II	624
Aphorism "Beethoven"	Henriques	II	637
March	Nicodé	II	640
Allemande	Handel	II	642
Cantilène	Salomé	II	644
Balletto	Martini	II	648
Petite Marche, Op. 20, No. 10	Cui	II	650
Mosaïque, Op. 20, No. 7	Cui	II	653
Canzonetta	Hollaender	II	656
Song of the Lark, Op. 39, No. 22	Tschaikowsky	II	658
Cradle Song	Kjerulf	II	660
Serenade	Drigo	II	663
Novellozza	Godard	II	666
Humoresque	Rheinberger	II	670
Mazurka, Op. 7, No. 1	Chopin	II	674
Bolero	Moszkowski	II	676
Berceuse	von Fielitz	II	680
Serenata	Moszkowski	II	682
Valsette	Borowski	II	685
Dance of the Elves	de Benedictis	II	688
The Old Mother	Grieg	II	692
Hunting Song, Op. 19, No. 3	Mendelssohn	II	695
Spring Dance	Grieg	II	698
Serenade Badine	Gabriel-Marie	II	700
Gopak	Moussorgsky	III	705
Crescendo	Lasson	III	708
A Sketch	Dubois	III	711
Moment Musical, Op. 94, No. 3	Schubert	III	714
Solfeggietto	C. P. E. Bach	III	716
Londonderry Air	*From* County Derry	III	720
Pictures for Children	Rebikoff	III	722
March of the Little Tin Soldiers	Pierné	III	728
Pas des Amphores	Chaminade	III	733
Ballet Scene	Busoni	III	738
The Musical Box	Liebich	III	742
Punchinello	Herbert	III	748
Berceuse	Liadow	III	752
Polka ("The Golden Age")	Shostakovitch	III	757
On the Beautiful Blue Danube	Strauss	III	760
A Nursery Tale, Op. 39, No. 19	Tschaikowsky	III	766
Chanson Triste, Op. 40, No. 2	Tschaikowsky	III	768
Boat Song	P. Scharwenka	III	771
Prelude, Op. 11, No. 13	Scriabine	III	776
Bohemian Dance, Op. 39, No. 14	Tschaikowsky	III	778
Romance	Moszkowski	III	779
A la Schumann, Op. 20, No. 4	Cui	III	782
Sonata, *D major* (Finale)	Haydn	III	784
Knave Rupert, Op. 68, No. 12	Schumann	III	788
The Nun (Soeur Monique)	Couperin	III	790
Scarf Dance	Chaminade	III	794
Oxen Minuet	Haydn	III	796
Nocturne No. V	Leybach	III	798
Sonatina, Op. 45, No. 1	Mortimer Wilson	III	804
Sonatina, Op. 45, No. 2	Mortimer Wilson	III	813

GRADE IV

Title	Composer	Vol.	Page
Andante	J. C. Bach	III	826
Song of the Volga Boatman	Russian	III	830
Tarantelle	Heller	III	832
Gavotte, *G minor*	Bach	III	841
Solvejg's Song, Op. 55, No. 4	Grieg	III	844
Romance	Rimsky-Korsakoff	III	848
Turkish March (Sonata, *A major*)	Mozart	III	850
Spring Song, Op. 62, No. 6	Mendelssohn	III	854
A Song	Jensen	III	858
Scherzo Rustique, Op. 20, No. 12	Cui	III	861
Minuet, Op. 14, No. 1	Paderewski	III	864
Idilio	Lack	III	869
Chansonette	Troiani	III	872
Minuetto e Trio, *B minor*	Schubert	III	874
Valse Caprice	de Falla	III	876
Mazurka, Op. 20, No. 11	Cui	III	882

LIST OF GRADE III AND IV COMPOSITIONS

Title	Composer	Vol.	Page
Humoreske	Dvorak	III	886
Andante Cantabile, from Op. 11	Tschaikowsky	III	890
Chant sans paroles	Tschaikowsky	III	896
Butterfly, Op. 43, No. 1	Grieg	III	899
Minuet, from Symphony in *G minor*	Mozart	III	904
Valse Bleue	Margis	III	906
Valse Mignonne	Schütt	III	912
Reverie	Richard Strauss	III	918
Murmuring Zephyrs	Jensen	III	920
Polish Dance	Scharwenka	III	926
Etude Mignonne	Schütt	III	930
Salut d'amour	Elgar	III	934
Pierrette	Chaminade	III	938
Nocturne, Op. 15, No. 3	Chopin	III	944
Wedding March, Op. 61, No. 6	Mendelssohn	III	948
Nocturne, Op. 55, No. 1	Chopin	III	952
Cradle Song, Op. 24, No. 3	MacDowell	III	957
Träumerei, Op. 15, No. 7	Schumann	III	960
Norwegian Bridal Procession	Grieg	III	962
Prelude, Op. 17, No. 4	Scriabine	III	968
Intermezzo, from "Cavalleria Rusticana"	Mascagni	III	969
A la biene aimée	Schütt	III	972
Prelude, Op. 28, No. 20	Chopin	III	977
March, from "Tannhäuser"	Wagner	III	978
Coronation March, from "The Prophet"	Meyerbeer	III	984
Souvenir	Drdla	III	988
Pizzicati, from "Sylvia"	Delibes	III	991
Bébé s'endort	Oswald	III	994
Prelude, *F major*	Bach	III	997
Slumber Song, Op. 124, No. 6	Schumann	III	998
Mazurka, Op. 56, No. 2	Chopin	III	1002
May Night	Palmgren	III	1005
Song without Words, Op. 62, No. 1	Mendelssohn	III	1008
Gigue, *B-flat major*	Bach	III	1011
Valse, Op. 39, No. 15	Brahms	III	1014
Mazurka, Op. 59, No. 3	Chopin	III	1016
Gavotte, *D minor*	Bach	III	1023
L'Angelus	C. Godard	III	1026
Orientale	Cui	III	1030
Bagatelle, Op. 33, No. 6	Beethoven	III	1032
Humoresque, Op. 10, No. 2	Tschaikowsky	III	1034
Barcarolle, "June"	Tschaikowsky	III	1039
Humoresque, Op. 6, No. 3	Grieg	III	1045
First Sorrow, Op. 52, No. 11	Kopylow	III	1046
Gigue, *D major*	Galuppi	III	1048
Valse, Op. 64, No. 2	Chopin	III	1051
To Spring, Op. 43, No. 6	Grieg	IV	1057
Valse Bluette	Drigo	IV	1062
The Last Spring, Op. 34, No. 2	Grieg	IV	1065
Serenade	Pierné	IV	1068
Second Gavotte	Godard	IV	1073
Priest's March, from "Athalia"	Mendelssohn	IV	1078
Erotik, Op. 43, No. 5	Grieg	IV	1083
Gymnopedie, No. II	Satie	IV	1086
Mazurka, Op. 33, No. 4	Chopin	IV	1088
Prelude, Op. 28, No. 15	Chopin	IV	1095
Rondo, *A minor*	Mozart	IV	1100
Warum, Op. 12, No. 3	Schumann	IV	1110
Melodie, Op. 16, No. 2	Paderewski	IV	1112
Valse, Op. 34, No. 1	Chopin	IV	1116
Chants du Voyageur, Op. 5	Paderewski	IV	1127
Mazurka, Op. 63, No. 1	Chopin	IV	1140
Harmonious Blacksmith	Handel	IV	1144
Song without Words, Op. 53, No. 3	Mendelssohn	IV	1152
Song without Words, Op. 53, No. 4	Mendelssohn	IV	1160
Nocturne, Op. 9, No. 2	Chopin	IV	1166
Prelude, Op. 1, No. 1	Szymanowski	IV	1169
Mazurka, Op. 6, No. 1	Chopin	IV	1172
Berceuse	Karganoff	IV	1176
Song without Words, Op. 19, No. 1	Mendelssohn	IV	1179
Danse Grotesque	de Benedictis	IV	1184
Postludium, Op. 13, No. 10	von Dohnanyi	IV	1189
Prelude	Cui	IV	1192
Sonata, *A major*	Paradisi	IV	1196
Romanze, Op. 28, No. 2	Schumann	IV	1204
The Flatterer	Chaminade	IV	1208
On the Silent Forest Path	Richard Strauss	IV	1211
Ghosts, Op. 15, No. 12	Schytte	IV	1216
Bourrée, *B minor*	Bach-Saint-Saens	IV	1219
The Butterfly	Lavallée	IV	1222
Romance, Op. 10, No. 6	Rachmaninoff	IV	1230
Mazurka	Debussy	IV	1232
Vals d'amour	Soro	IV	1238
Polonaise Militaire, Op. 40, No. 1	Chopin	IV	1240
Suite, *G minor*	Handel	IV	1244
Sonata, *D major*	Galuppi	IV	1250
Spanish Dance, Op. 5, No. 5	Granados	IV	1257
Intermezzo et Valse Lente	Delibes	IV	1262
Berceuse	Schytte	IV	1266
Romance, *D-flat*	Sibelius	IV	1270
Serenade	Sinding	IV	1275
Gavotte, from "Iphigenie in Aulis"	Gluck-Brahms	IV	1278
The Prophet Bird, Op. 82, No. 7	Schumann	IV	1282
Valse Triste	Sibelius	IV	1286
Reverie	Schütt	IV	1292
Mazurka, Op. 50, No. 1	Chopin	IV	1296
Nocturne, Op. 16	Paderewski	IV	1300
Sonata, *A major*	Scarlatti	IV	1305
Capriccio, *E major*	Scarlatti	IV	1312
Romance sans Paroles	Saint-Saens	IV	1318
Slavic Dance	Dvorak	IV	1321
Erotikon No. II	Sjögren	IV	1328
Notturno, Op. 54, No. 4	Grieg	IV	1332
Les demons s'amusent	Rebikoff	IV	1336
Zortzico	Albeniz	IV	1338
Tando, *D major*	Albeniz	IV	1343
Czardas, Op. 24, No. 4	MacDowell	IV	1346
Humoreske, Op. 24, No. 1	MacDowell	IV	1354

LIST OF GRADE III AND IV COMPOSITIONS

Title	Composer	Vol.	Page
Humoreske, Op. 18, No. 2	MacDowell	IV	1358
Barcarolle, Op. 18, No. 1	MacDowell	IV	1364
Romance, Op. 44, No. 1	Rubinstein	IV	1369
Waltz, Op. 54, No. 1	Dvorak	IV	1372
Yearning	Smetana	IV	1376
The Angelus	Lacombe	IV	1380
La Coquette	Borowski	IV	1382
Fantasia, *C minor*	Bach	IV	1386
Elegie	Nollet	IV	1390
Fantasia, *D minor*	Mozart	IV	1394
The Juggler (Le Jongleur)	Godard	IV	1400
Chant d'amour, Op. 10, No. 2	Paderewski	IV	1406
Serenade, Op. 3	Rachmaninoff	V	1409
Moment Musical, Op. 94, No. 2	Schubert	V	1414
Poëme	Fibich	V	1419
Renouveau (Etude)	Godard	V	1420
Notturno	Respighi	V	1427
Scherzino, Op. 10, No. 3	Paderewski	V	1434
Scherzo in Canon Form	Jadassohn	V	1438
Minuet, *D major*	Mozart	V	1440
Consolation, *E major*	Liszt	V	1442
Prelude, Op. 3, No. 2	Rachmaninoff	V	1447
Aphorism "Moderne"	Henriques	V	1452
Allegro Moderato, from "Près de la mer"	Arensky	V	1454
Twilight	Stcherbatcheff	V	1458
Nocturne (Nachtstück)	Schumann	V	1461
Sparks (Etincelles)	Moszkowski	V	1464
Morning (Peer Gynt Suite)	Grieg	V	1474
Ase's Death (Peer Gynt Suite)	Grieg	V	1478
Anitra's Dance (Peer Gynt Suite)	Grieg	V	1480
In the Hall of the Mountain King	Grieg	V	1483
Cracovienne Fantastique	Paderewski	V	1487
Henry VIII Dances	German	V	1494
Spinning Song, Op. 67, No. 4	Mendelssohn	V	1510
Rondo, Op. 51, No. 1	Beethoven	V	1517
Rustle of Spring	Sinding	V	1526
Intermezzo, Op. 76, No. 7	Brahms	V	1534
Nocturne, Op. 27, No. 2	Chopin	V	1536
On the Guitar	Moszkowski	V	1544
In the Village	Moussorgsky	V	1553
Aragonaise (from "Le Cid")	Massenet	V	1558
Peasant Dance	Beethoven	V	1562
Liebestraum	Liszt	V	1566
Impromptu, Op. 90, No. 2	Schubert	V	1573
Wedding Day at Troldhaugen	Grieg	V	1586
Valse Fantastique	Glazounoff	V	1597
Polonaise, Op. 26, No. 1	Chopin	V	1604
Troïka en Traineaux	Tschaikowsky	V	1609
Kammenoi Ostrow	Rubinstein	V	1614
Hungarian Dances, I, II, III, V	Brahms	V	1621
Prelude Op. 28, No. 17	Chopin	V	1638
Sunday Morning at Glion	Bendel	V	1643
Prelude, Op. 9, No. 1 (for the Left Hand)	Scriabine	V	1648
Tango Burlesco	Levy	V	1650
Caprice	Max Reger	V	1656
Caprice, Op. 43, No. 4	Arensky	V	1668
Arabesque	Leschetizky	V	1662
Rondo Capriccioso, Op. 14	Mendelssohn	V	1666
Waltzes, Op. 39, 1 to 10	Brahms	V	1679
Humoreske, Op. 10, No. 5	Rachmaninoff	V	1689
Seguidilla	Albeniz	V	1704
Witches' Dance, Op. 17, No. 2	MacDowell	V	1710
Prelude, Op. 32, No. 11	Rachmaninoff	V	1720
Barcarolle, *F minor*	Rubinstein	V	1698
Prelude, Op. 28, No. 3	Chopin	V	1723
Prelude, Op. 28, No. 1	Chopin	V	1726
Prelude, Op. 28, No 21	Chopin	V	1728
Six Poems after Heine	MacDowell	V	1730
Valse Lente, from "Coppelia"	Delibes	V	1752
Impromptu, Op 28, No. 2	Reinhold	V	1756